Nawa Yogini Tantra

With kind regards, ॐ and prem

Swami Niranjan

Nawa Yogini Tantra

Swami Muktananda

Under the Guidance of
Swami Satyananda Saraswati

Yoga Publications Trust, Munger, Bihar, India

Published by Bihar School of Yoga
    First edition 1977
    Second (revised) edition 1983
    Reprinted 1998

Published by Yoga Publications Trust
    Reprinted 2003, 2004, 2006, 2007

ISBN: 81-85787-42-5

Publisher and distributor: Yoga Publications Trust, Ganga Darshan, Munger, Bihar, India.

Website: www.yogavision.net

Printed at Thomson Press (India) Limited, New Delhi, 110001

Dedication

*In humility we offer this dedication to
Swami Sivananda Saraswati, who initiated
Swami Satyananda Saraswati into the secrets of yoga.*

Contents

To all the women
  of all places, East and West
  of all ages, old to young
who serve Swami Satyananda
who will serve him
and who have served him
  in his parivrajak life
  in ashram life
  in his wider mission
as sannyasin disciples and lay devotees
to all these women
from whom he has learned so much
who have, above all,
nurtured in him the equipoise
that brings enlightenment.

Women and
Spirituality

Women and Spirituality

by Swami Satyananda Saraswati

In tantra there are two important poles of energy known as
Shiva and Shakti. In fact, Shiva and Shakti have various
spheres of existence and operation in the cosmos and in the
individual. In the ordinary human society man and woman
represent Shiva and Shakti respectively. In the universal
mind, time and space represent Shiva and Shakti aspects. In
spiritual life, mind and prana represent Shiva and Shakti. In
hatha yogic texts, these two shaktis are known as ida and
pingala. Ida represents the consciousness and pingala
represents the life force, or prana.

These two shaktis are the opposite poles of energy.
Ordinarily, they are never together, but at the time of
creation, they meet at a point of union on every sphere. In
the universal mind, time and space come together at the
nucleus, and when they unite then the explosion takes place
in matter. Here, time is represented by plus energy and
space by minus energy.

Aspects of awakening

In ordinary human society, man and woman are the two
different poles of energy. These energy poles have been
discussed in detail in the ancient tantric tradition. You may
have seen a photograph of Kali standing practically naked,
with one foot placed on Shiva, who is flat on the ground. She
has a ferocious expression, a blood stained tongue and a

3

mala of 108 human skulls. That is Kali in the awakened state. You may also have come across some pictures, though they are very rare, of Shiva seated in lotus posture. Half of his body is Shiva and half is Shakti. Then you may have seen the picture of Shiva and Parvati sitting in the position of guru and disciple. Shiva is seated in lotus posture, and Parvati is seated on a lower platform. Shiva is instructing her in the secrets of tantra. These are three examples. The fourth you may also have heard about. About 110 miles from Munger is a very important centre of tantra known as Tarapeetha. There you can see Lord Shiva sucking at the breast of Shakti.

These are the relationships between Shiva and Shakti at different levels of evolution and awakening. At one point, Shakti is the disciple and Shiva is the guru: that is, woman is the disciple and man is the guru. At another level, they are not at all different. Shiva and Shakti are intertwined together in one body, one frame and one idea. At yet another level of evolution, Shakti is supreme and Shiva is subservient. Now, this is the philosophical interpretation of the stages of awakening of the inherent shakti in everybody.

Spiritual awareness of the woman
In the tantric tradition, the woman is considered to be higher than the man so far as the tantric initiations are concerned. This should by no means be understood as a social claim. It is purely a spiritual attitude in relation to the evolution of higher consciousness. The frame of a woman, her emotions, and her psychic evolution is definitely higher than that of a man. Awakening of the spiritual force (kundalini) is much easier in the body of a woman than in the body of a man.

Besides this, there is another important point that we have to understand. Generally, a man who goes into the deeper realms of mind and comes out, is not able to bring those experiences back with him, but a woman can. It seems to me that there is very little difference between a woman's inner and outer awareness. When you go very deep into your consciousness, you have certain experiences. But when

4

you return from that deeper state of mind to gross awareness, a veil falls in between those experiences and the conscious mind. In a woman this veil does not fall. Apart from this, the psychic being of a woman is highly charged with spiritual awareness. The external expression that you will find in a woman or a girl – love for beauty, tenderness, sympathy, understanding, are expressions of her inner state. I usually make a joke. I say, if all women leave this world, it would become a desert. There would be no colours, perfumes, smiles or beauty. This indicates that the inner awareness of a woman is very receptive and ready to explode.

In the realm of kundalini yoga also, the woman's body is charged by a particular centre. Mooladhara chakra in the male body is intricately situated in a very congested area. Men do moola bandha and still nothing happens. But in a woman's body, you can even touch mooladhara with your fingers. Therefore, awakening can take place in a woman's body much more quickly than in the body of a man.

Another important point is that woman has always been the main transporter of energy and man the medium. The woman may not be your wife: she could be your mother, daughter or disciple. Mary was Christ's mother. The Mother of Aurobindo Ashram was a disciple. In the same way, in the tantric tradition, there is the story of the sixty four yoginis. The word yogini is the feminine gender of yogi. Now, these yoginis are worshipped all over India. There are sixty four temples dedicated to the sixty four aspects of feminine energy. One of these is in Assam, another is in Calcutta at Kali Ghat.

Role in tantra

When we study the books on tantra, we clearly come across one central theme: Shakti is the creator, and Shiva is instrumental. Shiva has never been considered as a creator. In vama marga, it is Shakti who is important, not only in sexual life but in spiritual practices, carrying out the processes of creation and in conducting most of the spiritual rituals. Amongst Hindus, all the rituals, religious and otherwise, are mainly conducted by women; men have to sit quietly. Woman is the commissioner; man is the participant. Whether it is an ordinary social ceremony, a religious ceremony, the worship of a deity, or a day of fasting, it is the woman who introduces it. The man just has to follow her. This is the tradition in India known as initiation from the woman to the man.

What is vama marga? It is the spiritual path which can be practised along with your partner. The second division is called kaulachara. This involves the mother giving initiation to the son. The north of Bihar particularly is the centre for this type of initiation. Up to the borders of Nepal in the north, Assam in the east, and Uttar Pradesh in the west, is the area in which the kaulachara initiation is prevalent, even today. According to this tradition, the son considers his mother a goddess. Every morning, just as Christians go to church on Sundays or Hindus go to the temple and bow down before the deity, or do some sort of prostration, in the same way, the son approaches his mother. This is not just a social respect that he pays to the elders of the family. It is a spiritual adoration which is performed, not because she is his mother, but because she is his guru.

The same thing is done in vama marga as well, but here it is not the son, but the partner who prostrates before the woman. Then the spiritual mark or mark of blessing has to be given. Here the woman places this mark on the man; it is not he who places it on her.

So these are the two important roles in which the woman is involved in tantra. It is a sad mistake to consider the woman in tantra only as a sexual partner. Sexual life is important, but it is not the only relationship that can exist between a man and woman. After all, your mother is also a woman, so too is your daughter, as well as your wife.

The woman comes first

In tantra the role of initiator is shifted from the male to the female. Ramakrishna Paramahamsa always considered his wife Sarada as devi, or goddess. In Sanskrit devi means

6

illumined or illustrious. When Ramakrishna was married, he was very young and his wife was still a child, but he regarded her as the Divine Mother. That is how he always behaved towards her, and that is what he considered her to be.

In the scheme of evolution, Shakti comes first, and Shiva comes next. With this attitude, if you go on in spiritual life, either with your wife, daughter or disciple, then you have to see that she is the activator and you are the participant in every sphere. Even if a man has realized the higher awareness, he will still have difficulty in communicating that to others if he does not bring a woman into the picture.

Hypothesis in hatha yoga

In tantra it is also to be remembered that there is another path called dakshina marga or vedic tantra. Here the woman is not necessary, neither as daughter, mother or wife, because the aspirant is considered to have both forces within himself. Ida is feminine and pingala is masculine. Union between the mental and pranic forces is equivalent to union between a man and woman. That is the hypothesis in hatha yoga.

Ida is Shakti and pingala is Shiva. When they unite in ajna chakra, that is the real union. The seat of Shakti is in mooladhara. The seat of Shiva is in sahasrara. Shiva is in eternal yoga nidra there, inactive, unconcerned, nameless and formless. He has nothing to do with destruction or creation. His consciousness is homogeneous and total. There is no vibration in sahasrara. Shakti is in mooladhara, and by the practices of yoga, you awaken her. She becomes aroused and makes headway through sushumna up to ajna. When Shakti reaches ajna chakra, union takes place.

Dance of Shiva

This union occurs when the two poles of energy come together. When you press the switch, there is light, because the wires of the switch are uniting. In the same way, in ajna chakra, when union takes place, the explosion also simultaneously occurs. Then the energy created in ajna chakra moves

7

up to sahasrara chakra. There Shiva and Shakti unite with each other, and when they unite, Shiva begins to dance. Perhaps you have seen a photo of Nataraja. That is the symbolic expression of the awakened Shiva.

When Shiva wakes up from his profound yoga nidra, then he begins to dance. I am not talking about a man, but a force. The awakening of that force in man is symbolized by the dance of Shiva in the form of Nataraja. Then Shakti and Shiva descend together through the same path to moola-dhara. Both come down together to the mundane level, the gross plane. That is the path of the saints who come down and reach us from time to time. If you happen to read the philosophy of Sri Aurobindo, you will understand about the awakening of energy and its union with Shiva, both of them dancing together and then coming down to our plane of existence. That is why in kriya yoga we have ascending and descending passages – arohan and awarohan.

New society
Now, the role of women and spirituality has been defined, but the position of women in the modern cultures is far from this. People all over the world are fighting with their own guilt and sin. If you wish to resurrect the pristine position of women today, then the whole attitude will have to be changed. In fact, our social structure will have to be based on a new concept of religious realities, in which the role of woman in mankind's spiritual evolution is fully understood and accepted. This is absolutely necessary for the emergence of a new society.

A Woman's Body

The description *female* is a biological label applied to those members of any species who bear the young. However, in general use it has taken on much wider connotations and becomes confused with characteristics other than the purely biological. Nowadays, to be born female implies that the child is not only physically equipped for maternity, but also that she will necessarily exhibit certain psychological behavioural characteristics.

Exactly what these traits and behaviours are differs from culture to culture and from time to time within cultures. It is obvious, that they are not just a product of biology but also of social process. It is this that is conveyed when we use the word woman which implies not only a female body, but also the psychological characteristics of the whole mature person.

Within the different cultural images and ideals of women there is an outline that seems similar and enduring, and to trace this outline we shall first examine what it is to be female in the strictly biological sense.

The key

The key to the different developments in males and females can be found in the study of the simplest unit of living creatures – the cell. In each cell there are tiny thread-like structures called chromosomes. The chromosomes carry genes which encode the information that determines whether

9

a human organism will be male or female. In all normal human cells there are twenty-two pairs of chromosomes that determine non-sexual characteristics and they are all called X-chromosomes. There is one more pair that determines sex and related characteristics, giving twenty-three pairs.

Of the cells in the human body, all have the full twenty-three pairs of chromosomes except the female egg (ovum) and the male egg (sperm) – one of each is necessary to create a complete cell. The cell which is created at the time of conception is the basic unit from which all the body cells of the future human being arise.

Each female egg carries half the chromosomes for the new organism, and the female half of the sex determining pair is called the X-chromosome. The male sperm carries the remaining chromosome which may be either of the type called X or the type called Y. The sex of the child is determined by the sperm, for if it carries an X-chromosome the union with the ovum will produce an XX chromosome pair. In this case the new human being will have a female body. If the sperm carries a Y-chromosome, the pair will be XY and the new organism will be male.

Thus, we can see that of the forty-six chromosomes in the human body, forty-five are common to both sexes and only one chromosome is different. The variations that result from this have led most people to exaggerate the difference between the sexes, deluding themselves that difference is all and forgetting that the sexes have so much in common.

Female and male

Except for the reproductive organs, male and female bodies contain the same organ systems with very few, and negligible, differences. The most noticeable of these is the smaller lung capacity in females. The circulatory system is the same in both cases, although the female system seems to be stronger in that it is less susceptible to heart attack and related ailments. Females and males have identical nervous systems, although males are said to have the larger brain. However, considered in proportion to the total body weight, it is found that the female brain is actually larger.

Overall, the female has lighter and more delicate bones than the male. However their skeletons are so much alike that scientists seeking to identify a particular skeleton as male or female cannot do so beyond doubt. Generally, females have narrower and more sloping shoulders than males. Most men have hips narrower than their shoulders, most women have hips either slightly broader than, or about the same width as, their chest and shoulders. It is usually true that the legs in the female are shorter in proportion to total height than those of the male. In this case though, there is a great overlap that might well be affected by diet and kinds of exercise in childhood.

Females are generally not as heavily muscled as males, particularly in the chest region. Female muscle tissue contains a greater amount of fatty tissue and seldom develops either the size or the hardness of the muscles in male bodies. However, it is possible for female development to equal male musculature, if they constantly do the same work.

It is almost universally regarded that males are stronger and that females are 'the weaker sex'. This is repeated despite evidence that amongst humans the female is constitutionally stronger than the male. Females live longer, and in every age group the death rate for males is higher than for females. Fewer females suffer from ulcers and heart attacks, and it is thought now that susceptibility to heart problems in males is perhaps related to hormones produced by the testes. Statistics also show that women seem to be capable of enduring greater hardship and strain and that they are not as delicate physically as men. It has been said that 'men are the strong ones but women are the tough ones'.

The hormonal system

The endocrine system exists alongside the nervous system as another 'messenger system' which coordinates the various internal functions. It consists of various chemicals called hormones, which are secreted by special ductless glands directly into the bloodstream, then carried to all parts of the body. They have a tremendous influence on bodily growth, size and shape, and also moderate a woman's temperament, mental powers, attitudes, energy and personality.

These ductless glands are the pituitary, pineal, thyroid, parathyroid, pancreas, thymus, adrenal glands and gonads. Nearly all are found in pairs so that if one is damaged or diseased, the other can continue to meet the needs of the body. The action of each gland is intimately connected with that of all the others, and the interactions of the various hormones are an important aspect of this system. Thus, any disorder in even one gland will have considerable repercussions throughout a woman's body, and on her emotions.

The pituitary gland is a small pea-sized gland located at the base of the brain. This is the master gland which controls all the others through several specialized hormones, including those governing the female reproductive cycle. It also regulates the body's water and salt balance, hence this is the gland implicated in the periodic fluid retention experienced by many women in connection with the menstrual cycle. Located in the brainstem at the very top of the spinal cord, the pituitary is very sensitive to stress in both the nervous and hormonal systems. Disturbance of the pituitary may be felt in many parts of the body, and for a woman, especially in relation to the monthly cycle.

The pineal gland is responsible for smooth transition between various states of consciousness – from waking to sleeping, sleep to dream, and for psychic activity. This gland has a role to play in physical maturity for both boys and girls, and is related to emotional stability in adults. Deficiency of serotonin, a pineal hormone, is a precipitating factor in endogenous depression – a problem faced by many women.

The thyroid gland regulates metabolism, shapes body growth, and governs the composition of the blood. The thyroid paces our inner clockwork by activating or inhibiting various organs and systems. Shaped like a butterfly, it is located in the front of the neck on either side of the windpipe. An overactive thyroid causes weight loss, nervousness and irritability. An underactive thyroid may cause weight gain, lethargy and pessimism. Other cycles within the body are also adversely affected.

The parathyroid glands are very small glands, two on each side of the windpipe. Although encased within the thyroid, they act independently to regulate bone growth and distribution of calcium and phosphorous.

The thymus gland is located in the centre of the chest, and is particularly important in children, helping to regulate the growth pattern. Although of less significance in adults, it is now known to play a major role in our immune reactions to allergy and infection. Disturbances of the thymus result in low resistance and poor emotional stamina.

The adrenal glands are attached to the top of each kidney. The central part (medulla) produces adrenaline and noradrenaline which affect blood pressure, respiration, oxygen consumption and numerous other aspects of the 'fight or flight' reflex. Too much of these hormones can lead to high blood pressure and circulatory problems, digestive disorders, and to constant fear and anxiety. The adrenal cortex produces steroids which affect the liver, kidneys, reproductive organs, blood pressure, digestion of protein and mobilization of sugars and fats. Improper cortisone production is implicated in disease of any of these systems.

The pancreas contains the islets of langerhans which produce digestive juices and the hormone insulin which regulates blood sugar. Breakdown of insulin production causes diabetes, with its attendant complications.

The gonads are the glands of the reproductive system, the testes and prostate in males, the ovaries in females, producing the hormones necessary for sexual differentiation and maturity. In women the ovaries produce oestrogen and progesterone which moderate the menstrual cycle. Imbalance in these hormones leads to all kinds of reproductive system disorders, to emotional sensitivity, anxiety and depression.

In women the production of these hormones is regulated by feedback from several other glands, notably the pituitary, and is especially vulnerable to any kind of stress.

All hormones, including sex hormones, are present in both females and males, but the balance in each is different. All male hormones, including testosterone, are called androgens. Female hormones are called oestrogens. The adrenal glands in both sexes produce large quantities of both androgens and oestrogens. Oestrogens in males cannot be assigned any specific function, at the present time at least. Androgens are the trigger, in both sexes, for the physical conditions felt as sexual tensions.

Under the influence of the pituitary gland, the whole endocrine system and the interaction of the various hormones change at puberty. With the mature functioning of the testes, the balance of androgens to oestrogens in the male body is fifty-four percent to forty-six percent. In the female body, the ovaries determine the balance of androgens to oestrogens in the ratio of forty-six percent to fifty-four percent. In examining this situation, the fact of the great similarity between the sexes is just as striking as their differences.

However, it is the change in hormonal balance at puberty which brings about its development of the reproductive system and emphasizes the differentiation between men and women. In the male body the greater production of testosterone results in the maturation of the sexual organs, a deeper voice and the growth of body hair and beard. In the female body the predominance of oestrogen leads to the development of the breasts and the widening of the pelvis. It causes fat to be deposited in various parts of the body, giving the typical 'rounded' contour of the mature woman, and causes the voice to remain fairly high-pitched.

The hormone progesterone sets in motion the ovulation and menstrual cycle that continues for the greater part of a woman's life span. This cycle is perhaps the most dramatic aspect of female physiology, attuning a woman's body to a different rhythm from that of men.

Female bodies are activated by the same glands and hormones as male bodies, with the exception of the glands associated with reproduction. However, a woman's body is hormonally more complex than a man's. Not only is the endocrine balance in a constant state of flux due to the menstrual cycle, but all endocrine glands are intimately related, so that this continual change is reflected throughout a woman's body and in her emotions. For this reason, it is important that women should be familiar with the glandular system and its significance.

Reproductive system

Human females and males differ physically in their primary sex characteristics (genital organs) and in secondary sex characteristics such as the breasts of women and the greater body hair and lower voices of men, the differences in proportion of the bones and the distribution of body fat. The most obvious differences are in the sexual and reproductive organs which in females are the clitoris, vagina, uterus, the Fallopian tubes and the ovaries. The male reproductive system contains the penis, the testicles, the prostate gland, the vas deferens and the seminal vesicles. The female reproductive system consists of that group of organs which has for its object the bringing forth of young. The main components of this system are the ovaries, Fallopian tubes, the uterus (womb), the vagina and the clitoris.

The vulva: The external genitals are known as the vulva consisting of the clitoris and two sets of fleshy lips – the labia majora on the outside and the smaller labia minora on the inside, at the opening of the vagina. The clitoris is a tiny erectile organ at the very top of the vulva. It corresponds to the penis in the male in that it is extremely sensitive, it enlarges in size with excitation and is covered with a fold of skin like the foreskin. The clitoris is vital to sexual excitation and pleasure in the female, but does not play a part in reproduction.

The vagina: If the labia minora are separated, two openings are seen; a smaller one above (the urinary opening)

er one below for the vagina. The vagina is a tube-
ige which leads to the womb. The point where
wom... ...d vagina meet is the cervix. The vagina is about
three inches long, but capable of considerable extension.
The function of the vagina is to contain the penis of the male
and to provide a passage for the seminal fluid. During sexual
intercourse the cervix rises and the vagina lengthens towards
the back, forming a hollow into which the semen is deposited
as in a small pool. After intercourse, the cervix descends into
this pool, submerging itself in the seminal fluid which can
then flow into the uterus and the Fallopian tubes.

In most girls who have not had sexual intercourse there
is a thin membrane covering the vaginal opening. This is the
hymen or maidenhead which must be broken before full
sexual intercourse can take place. The breaking of the hymen
usually takes place during the first copulation but it may
have occurred before that time. The absence of a hymen
does not mean that a girl is not a virgin, although its presence
is a fairly sure sign that she is.

The uterus: The womb or uterus is a pear-shaped organ,
about three inches long, connected to the outer surface of
the body by the vagina. The uterine walls are made up of
some of the strongest muscles in the female body. These
muscles consist of an outer layer of membrane and an inner
mucus lining. The uterus is usually tilted forward, with the
mouth (cervix) towards the back. Once an egg is fertilized it
embeds itself in the uterus, and this organ can actually expand
to many times its original size in order to accommodate the
developing child.

The Fallopian tubes: On either side of the uterus, in the
abdomen, is a fine tube called the Fallopian tube, curving
outwards and terminating in a free, fringed, trumpet shaped
end. The end is placed close to the ovary and the egg passes
through this tube after leaving the ovary. The two Fallopian
tubes are about four inches long and no thicker than a hair
at the place where they enter the uterus. It takes the egg
three or four days to pass through the tubes. If unfertilized it

16

disintegrates before reaching the uterus. If fertilized it embeds itself in the uterine lining.

The ovaries: An ovary is approximately spherical in shape, about an inch long, and weighs three grams or so. There are two ovaries in the female body, one on each side of the uterus. The ovaries produce ova which are tiny, microscopic cells or eggs. An egg ripens and is released from one or other ovary in every period of about four weeks. It is thought that the ovaries alternate in production, but this is not certain. Occasionally it may happen that more than one egg is released and, if both are fertilized twins will be born. The process of releasing an ovum (one egg) is called ovulation. Under stimulus from the pituitary hormones the ovaries also produce the hormones oestrogen and progesterone, which govern the menstrual cycle.

The broad ligament: On each side, the Fallopian tube, the ovary, the uterine blood vessels and nerves lie together on a wide sheet of tissue known as the broad ligament, which passes from the uterus to the side wall of the pelvis. It consists of the same type of membrane lining the abdomen.

The breasts: The breasts are not directly involved in reproduction but provide the source of nourishment for the new-born child and act as indicators of body rhythms. The breasts are a pair of glands situated on either side of the chest. They contain special glandular tissue which produces and secretes milk. This milk is carried by a series of ducts to the nipple, which consists of erectile tissue and contains openings through which the infant sucks the milk. The secretion of milk is stimulated by the act of sucking. Breast milk confers some immunity on the infant as well as being suited to its needs and digestive capacities.

The breasts are very sensitive and the nipples respond to excitement by becoming erect and hard. It is not uncommon for the breasts to reflect the phases of the menstrual cycle. Many women find their breasts become larger and heavier just before menstruation begins, then returning to normal within a day or two.

The menstrual cycle

Any system is more than the sum of its parts, and this is especially true of the female reproductive system. Under the direction of the pituitary gland, this system functions to the hormonal rhythm that results in ovulation and menstruation, and which subtly influences a woman's health and emotions. You will find a full discussion of the menstrual cycle and its significance in a later chapter.

Antidote to fear

A woman should be familiar with the workings of her body as a whole, but in particular the reproductive system which is the prime characteristic of her biological femininity. According to yoga, this region is influenced by mooladhara chakra which is the seat of primal energy and one of the most important psychic centres. Sensitivity to the location of mooladhara is a prerequisite of many yogic practices.

The internal location of the reproductive organs does not lend itself to easy exploration and many women, even today, remain ignorant of the reasons for the periodic bodily changes they experience. This is compounded by the secrecy, shame and superstition that so often surround female sexuality. We have included this simple discussion in order to assist women to more sensitive and objective awareness of their bodies. However, standard physiology is only a framework for clarifying the personal perceptions that are the real foundation of a woman's knowledge of her body.

Sensitivity to, and understanding of, the signs of her body's functioning are an antidote to fear and an aid to every woman's confidence. Moreover, knowledge of the rhythms and workings of health is the basis of early detection of any disturbance of ill health. This kind of body awareness is available to every woman and a few have developed their sensitivity to such an extent that they can not only sense physical changes, but also the flow of subtle energy. Knowledge is power, and the power of sensitive control of her own body is each woman's birthright.

18

The Yoga Body

Yogic physiology is not the physiology of the physical body, but the physiology of the psychic or subtle body, dimensions of our existence unseen by the physical eye. It adds a new dimension to the catchcry 'biology is destiny' by charting the psychic biology that we exploit in achieving the goal of transcendental awareness. It is the knowledge of this subtle energy framework that enables every woman to understand the role of her physical body as a tool in the evolution of consciousness.

Pancha kosha

The esoteric physiology realized by yogis points out the existence of five dimensions of being within the human frame. These are known as the *pancha kosha*, the sheaths of the atman.

Kosha is a Sanskrit word meaning 'sheath'. If you put a glove on your hand, this is a sheath. To the yogic vision there are five such sheaths covering the atman, the spark of infinite consciousness which is the cause and core of our being. Moving outward from the atman, from invisible to visible, from subtle to gross, these sheaths are: anandamaya, vijnanamaya, manomaya, pranamaya and annamaya. In this context *maya* means 'composed of', and these sheaths or dimensions of existence are said to be composed respectively of bliss, intuition, intellect, energy and food.

19

Anandamaya kosha is the dimension of pure bliss. Vijnanamaya kosha is the sheath of higher knowledge which makes itself felt in the flash of intuition, the spark of genius. Manomaya kosha is the dimension of mind – containing intellect, memory, concept and reason. Pranamaya kosha is composed of prana, the vital energy that activates the body and motivates the mind. Annamaya kosha is the physical body, so called because of its dependence on 'anna', on grain or gross food.

All these sheaths or dimensions of being are interpenetrating and interacting. They are different expressions of the one radiant consciousness. They are not at all isolated except insofar as our awareness is limited to the more gross dimensions, therefore creating an artificial division between our 'natural' and 'supernatural' perceptions and capacities. All our sadhana is directed at enabling us to develop awareness of all five of these coverings or sheaths, and of the glorious atman beyond.

The differences between these dimensions are variations of refinement and expansion, for all are actually of the same substance. Each sheath is composed of energy, energy vibrating at different speeds. In the physical sheath the energy vibration is at its slowest. As we move through the koshas the vibration becomes faster and finer until it once again resolves itself back into pure consciousness. For energy is but the dynamic form of consciousness, and consciousness is the potential form of energy. It is for this reason that each level of our existence has its characteristic quality of perception, feeling, thought and awareness. The vibration of energy, of prana, is a reflection of the clarity, refinement and expanse of consciousness.

One way to understand this is to take the analogy of water. For the different vibrations of prana we will take the different states of water. Water as we generally experience it, is a liquid. Freeze it and it becomes solid, and we call it ice. Ice is solid water. In the same way, we can understand the physical body to be immobilized energy, 'frozen' energy, a state in which the energy moves so slowly that we don't even perceive it as energy.

When we heat ice, we speed up the energy within it, and ice becomes water. The characteristic expression of water is a flow. So too, in the pranamaya kosha, the prana flows in rivers of energy. If we heat the water further, we will get steam. As water moves more quickly than ice, so steam moves more quickly than water. Our thoughts also move with astonishing speed and the corresponding dimension of our being is the manomaya kosha. Steam is not only faster but also more potent than water. A small amount of steam can do much more work than the corresponding amount of water. Think of a pressure cooker, for instance, or the steam engine. Likewise the manomaya kosha is more powerful than the lower dimensions, it works more quickly, more forcefully and reaches much further.

Beyond steam we have ether. Ether is a very fine gas, a rarefied atmosphere. We can have an idea of the character of ether by recalling the experience of perfume. When someone enters the room wearing perfume, we can smell it immediately because the ether travels instantaneously in all directions. Likewise the vijnanamaya kosha is all pervading.

With anandamaya kosha our analogy falls short for there is nothing in the merely physical realm that can capture the essence of this state of being. Yet even such an indescribable, transcendental dimension of existence is part of our heritage waiting to be reclaimed by each and every one of us.

On the yogic path we often hear the expression 'raising the consciousness'. What is meant here is the expansion of awareness to embrace all the five koshas. When we practise sadhana, we increase the vibration and refinement of the energy, the prana, that constitutes our existence. With this, our perceptions and feelings, our thoughts and pre-occupations also become more refined and more expansive.

When the energy level is low and the vibration gross, we are aware almost exclusively of the physical body. All our feeling and thinking is concerned with the body, its desires and miseries. As we intensify our energy we raise the consciousness to higher and higher dimensions. We become aware of prana and the psychic realm of mind, we learn to control our thoughts and tap our creativity. Still higher we open ourselves to intuition and 'above the mind' experience, to the budding of spirituality.

Rivers of energy

The multidimensional energy pattern of the koshas is fed and pinned together by major currents or flows of prana. These pathways of pranic current in the body and mind are known as 'nadis'. For years and years, when people have translated the shastras from Sanskrit into English, nadi has been translated as 'nerve'. This is not accurate. The nadis are not the nervous system. Nadi means 'flow'. In Sanskrit the word for flow is nadi, anything that flows is nadi. What flows in it is something different, but the current of flow is called nadi. In a river water flows, in the nadis of the body, prana flows, energy is flowing.

Over and above the nervous system, we have a network of energy pathways or energy currents that are called nadis. We can think of these nadis as rivers of energy flowing in the body and the mind. Yoga's psychic physiology tells us that there are 72,000 nadis in the body. Of these fourteen are important, and of these fourteen there are three which are most important – ida, pingala and sushumna.

How are we to understand and discover these nadis? No doctor has ever yet found a nadi when performing an operation. We cannot put a nadi in a bottle. If we think of nadis as we think of blood vessels, arteries or even nerves, we will never find them. Yet, just because we cannot find a nadi on dissection does not mean that nadis do not exist.

If you cut my throat while I am talking you won't find any words in my throat. You cannot dissect a word, you cannot put a word in a specimen bottle, you cannot perform any operations for improving your grammar. Yet you have no doubt that words definitely exist and you have every confidence in your ability to use them. Similarly nobody can show us a thought. Although experts have performed a great deal of brain surgery, no one has yet been able to take a thought in his hands and hold it up for us to see. Yet you have no doubt that you are thinking, you do not doubt the impact of your thoughts on all that you do.

Now both speaking and thinking are currents, they are flows. Words are produced by a flow of breath that sets up a vibration in the vocal cords, it is a flow and a vibration – a kind of 'nadi'. A thought, also, is flow. On the most material level a thought is known to be a flow of chemicals and electrical impulses from one brain cell to the next. Although we cannot pinpoint the origin or the end of this flow, we are convinced about the fact of thinking.

As we gain sensitivity and insight and experience in yoga, we also become aware of the flow of energy that constitutes the nadis. When the windows are open in a room there will be a current of air flowing through that room. We cannot see this air current, but we can feel it. In the same way we can become sufficiently sensitive to feel the currents of prana in the body – the rivers of energy. When electricity is passing through the wires we don't see it. There seems to be no change in the wire, but if you put your finger in the electric socket then definitely you will feel the current. So it is with the nadis, the chakras and the other 'organs' of the subtle body. As we increase our sensitivity through sadhana, as we learn how to plug in to the energy socket, so we will be convinced about the nature and function of the rivers of pranic energy in our constitution. We will come to understand the nadis as pathways or currents of subtle energy – more subtle than the flow of the air in a room, more powerful than the flow of electricity.

Ida and Pingala

The three main nadis in our psychic constitution are ida, pingala and sushumna. Sometimes these rivers of energy are named after the sacred rivers Ganga, Jamuna and Saraswati.

Starting from a point a little below the base of the spine, ida nadi flows up the left side of the spinal column into the very centre of the head. From the same point of origin, pingala nadi flows along the right side of the spine to be reunited with ida in the midbrain. Sushumna nadi flows within the most subtle core of the spine.

In the hatha yoga texts, ida is referred to as chandra nadi and pingala as surya nadi, hinting at their complimentary nature. These two nadis have spheres of influence that are simultaneously physical, psychological and spiritual for they radiate in all the koshas from the physical body, through the mind to the subtle inner self.

On the physical level, the flow of prana in ida and pingala nadis can be correlated with the functioning of the autonomic nervous system. The dominance of ida nadi corresponds with the dominance of the parasympathetic (relaxing) nervous system, and dominance of pingala nadi with the sympathetic (activating) nervous system. When ida is flowing the breath will be more in the left nostril. When pingala is flowing the breath will be more in the right nostril.

On the psychological level, the flow of ida nadi is linked with what these days we might call right brain functioning; holistic thinking in pictures rather than words, intuition, receptivity, orientation towards one's inner world. Pingala is associated with left hemisphere; logic, analysis, verbal thinking, initiative, orientation towards the outer world. It could be said that ida provides the inspiration for action, and pingala provides the capacity to make this a reality through action in the world. Ida nadi is often called manovahini, the channel of manas shakti, mental energy or awareness. Pingala is called pranavahini, the channel of prana shakti, of vitality and life force. Pingala is associated with dynamic energy and ida with mental and psychic awareness.

The prana flowing in these two major currents is distributed through all the koshas, including the physical body, by a prolific network of smaller channels, also called nadis. In the Upanishads we are told there are 72,000 nadis

24

in the human organism responsible for the vitality of the body, clarity of mind and subtlety of consciousness.

Origin of disease

The yogis understand disease and illness in relation to the free flow or impediment of prana in the nadis. If prana is blocked at any point, there will be disease. Illness will also result if there is an excess or a deficiency of energy within the system. Health and wellbeing result when prana is freely distributed and properly balanced in every dimension of our being. Yoga is effective in maintaining and restoring optimum health to the whole system precisely because yoga practices are specifically designed for the redistribution and harmonization of prana.

The blockages and imbalances in the flow of energy that manifest as disease in the physical body may originate in any one of the koshas. Therefore the cause may be physical, emotional, mental, psychic or spiritual in nature. The exact symptoms of illness will depend on which nadis are consequently blocked. Understanding this, we can understand how our various ills and discomforts of the body may have their root in mental or emotional turmoil, or in neglect or frustration of the inner life.

Sushumna nadi

When ida, pingala and all the minor nadis are fully purified, when all blockages and resistances are removed and the flow of prana is in perfect balance and harmony, a third nadi comes into operation. This is sushumna, the channel of spiritual energy.

The aim of yoga sadhana is to balance ida and pingala, to balance the mental and the vital forces, to balance the receptive and the creative energies – literally to develop a balanced personality. When this is achieved, sushumna nadi becomes active and we gain access to a finer and more potent energy, a truly creative spirituality. It is when transcendental awareness under the name of kundalini shakti, flows in the passage of sushumna that we experience the expansive states of consciousness that give rise to spiritual insight and illumination.

Rings of power

As more and more energy begins to flow in sushumna nadi different aspects of our personality begin to unfold. This unfoldment comes through the greater activation of the psychic energy centres, known as chakras.

Our psychic physiology reveals that while sushumna nadi flows straight and true to the very top of the head, ida and pingala do not. We can think of ida and pingala as tributaries to the main flow of sushumna, and these two tributaries follow a winding, meandering course from left to right, right to left across the spine.

Often pingala curves to the left, and exactly opposite ida curves to the right, so that ida and pingala flow into one another at several important points. These meeting points are precisely at the places where each nadi crosses the spine, thus merging for a moment in sushumna. By coming to understand these intersections of the nadis, the confluence of the rivers of prana, we can also gain some insight into the nature of the chakras.

Wherever two rivers come together, at every place where a small stream enters a bigger stream, wherever a tributary flows into the major river – there you will see a whirlpool. So also where the currents of energy in the body meet, there are whirlpools. At each junction of ida, pingala and sushumna there will be a whirlpool, a round, circular movement of energy. These circular formations where the subtle energy flows around and around with great speed and fantastic power, these wheels of energy are called chakras. If we can glimpse the nadis as rivers of energy, then it is possible also to glimpse the mysterious chakras of kundalini yoga – and we see the chakras as vortices or whirlpools where the physical, mental and spiritual energies merge.

The chakras

There are four places where the rivers of ida, pingala and sushumna merge: at the tailbone, behind the navel, behind the heart, behind the throat. Add to these the source point of the nadis, in the perineum, and their end point in the midbrain. Altogether we have six junctions where the nadis flow each into the other. At each of these junctions there is a whirlpool of energy, called a chakra. There are thousands of minor chakras in the body, but these six are the most important. They are mooladhara at the perineum in men, at the opening of the womb in women; swadhisthana at the tailbone, manipura behind the navel, anahata behind the chest, vishuddhi behind the throat and ajna in the midbrain.

Each chakra has what is called a 'trigger point' in the front of the body. When we concentrate on this point, it helps us to become aware of the chakra itself. The chakras influence the nervous and endocrine systems of the physical body through the association of each chakra with a specific nerve plexus and a particular gland. Through these physical counterparts, the chakras energize all the organs of the body. The chakras are also concerned with certain psychological attitudes, thus acting as a bridge between body and mind. Primarily these vortices of concentrated energy act as storage, amplification and distribution centres for prana, and their full functioning is vital both to our physical well-being and our spiritual unfoldment.

Mooladhara chakra is the seat of primal energy, the source of both our sensuality and spirituality. Mooladhara is the point of origin for ida, pingala and sushumna and its trigger point in women is at the cervix where the vagina joins the womb. It represents the instinctive mind and with swadhisthana governs the reproductive system.

Swadhisthana chakra has its trigger point at the pubic bone. It governs a woman's reproductive and urinary systems through the sacral plexus and the ovaries. It is the threshold of the unconscious mind with its store of desires and inhibitions, talents and intuitions, demons and deities.

27

Manipura chakra is the centre of vitality and is triggered by awareness at the navel. Its corresponding nerve junction is the solar plexus and it is linked with the adrenal glands above the kidneys. Manipura governs the digestive system and is the major distributor of physical energy. Initiative, charisma and heroism are the attributes of this chakra.

Anahata chakra has its trigger point in the centre of the chest, and regulates the heart and respiratory system. Through the cardiac plexus its glandular counterpart is the thymus which plays a role in fighting infections. This is our emotional heart, concerned with acceptance of self and others, with emotional expression. When fully awakened it bestows universal love and compassion.

Vishuddhi chakra is the centre of purification in the throat. Concerned with the cervical plexus and thyroid gland, it bestows insight and discrimination.

Ajna chakra, the third eye of Shiva, is triggered by awareness at the eyebrow centre. Its physical medium is the pineal gland which regulates changes in consciousness from waking to sleep, sleep to dream, depression to optimism. Awakening ajna unfolds the higher powers of mind and the psychic receptivity through which the guidance of guru and higher self is intuited.

Linking body and mind

The chakras form an energy link that embraces body and mind in a single pattern of pranic energy. If there is any disturbance in the physical body due to irregular routine, incorrect diet or haphazard lifestyle, this will also cause some uneasiness in the mind. For this reason, when a woman's menstrual cycle is irregular, she will also feel some emotional repercussion in the form of anxiety or depression. On the other hand, where fear, frustration or guilt cause emotional turmoil, this disturbs the pranas of the mind. Such disturbance is reflected through swadhisthana chakra and its nervous and hormonal connections, and these disharmonies of mind become visible as irregularities in the physical body.

The chakras are sometimes called padma, or lotuses, each having a specific number of petals. These 'petals' are actually subsidiary nadis branching off from ida and pingala through that particular chakra. If there is any blockage or imbalance in these nadis, it will manifest as some physical disturbance in the organs governed by that chakra.

For instance, swadhisthana chakra has six petals. This means there are six nadis travelling out from swadhisthana to the various organs under its influence. If there is any excess or deficiency of pranic energy in these nadis, a woman will experience some kind of complaint of the urinary or reproductive system. Conversely, any reproductive or urinary system problem may be overcome by purification of these nadis through the asanas, pranayamas and other practices known to affect the activities of swadhisthana chakra. We can see that no practice of yoga is only physical or only mental. All yoga practices are multidimensional and guide us in all our complexity towards wholeness and harmony.

Flowering of spirituality

In most of us, the chakras are operating at only a fraction of their capacity. As the nadis are cleared of obstruction and more energy begins to flow in sushumna, so the chakras become more active. These subtle lotuses bloom, and we experience radiant physical health and abundant energy.

Yet more importantly, as the chakras unfold, so their corresponding qualities blossom in our personality. Attitudes, perspectives and talents that were previously dormant, only potential, now begin to show themselves in all our actions and interactions. The personality is gradually transformed as the dark sleeping regions of mind and soul are flooded with energy and light.

The fully developed transcendental personality is symbolized by sahasrara chakra, above the top of the head. The flowering of this thousand petalled lotus represents the enlightened soul and the countless ways our creative spirituality illumines our lives.

29

The blooming of all our capacities through the progressive awakening of the chakras is the ultimate goal of yoga, bringing every woman health, happiness and self-realization. The experience of this superconscious state is called samadhi, and takes place when kundalini rises from mooladhara, through the chakras along sushumna, to sahasrara. This union of Shiva and Shakti, the union of male and female in one body, is regarded by yogis as the highest state of our existence: the transcendence of petty differences in an ecstatic state of true humanity.

The Menstrual Cycle

The universe sings and dances to many rhythms – the long, slow wearing down of mountains; the steady march of the seasons; the staccato alternation of day and night; the wheeling of the sun, the advance and retreat of the moon. To live in a woman's body, especially, is to share in this flux and flow of the cosmos because a woman's awareness is constantly drawn to the natural pattern of fertility reflected in her own menstrual cycle.

This heightened awareness is a constant quiet theme of appreciation of our links with the infinite, and we should not allow it to degenerate into morbid preoccupation with the body. Too many women allow their consciousness to be limited to their bodies. Consciously or unconsciously, they always see themselves as sick, anxiously watching for the slightest variation in their cycle, worrying and fretting at the slightest twinge of pain, real or imagined.

An observant attitude to our bodies is an aid to health, but it must be based on proper knowledge and confidence. We must learn to trust our bodies. Our physical frame is a masterpiece of nature's handiwork, strong and gracefully integrated. It functions harmoniously under most circumstances, without any interference from ourselves. The human body is a self-regulating mechanism that is constantly adjusting itself in tune with its own needs and capacities.

Menstrual cycle

The menstrual cycle is a sequence of events that occurs once in a month in a sexually mature female. From *menarche* (first menstruation) to *menopause* (cessation of menstruation) it is a constant repetitive pattern. The beginning of each cycle is initiated by a hormone called the *follicle stimulating hormone* (FSH) produced by the pituitary gland at the base of the brain. This stimulates the ovary to produce a follicle containing a human egg. As the follicle matures, it in turn secretes oestrogen which prepares the lining of the uterus to receive the fertilized egg. Oestrogen also affects the pituitary so that it secretes *lutenizing hormone* (LH). When these two together reach a particular balance in the body (about the fourteenth day) the mature follicle releases the developed egg into one of the Fallopian tubes.

After the egg is ejected, the follicle is called the *corpus luteum* (yellow body) which is stimulated by LH to produce progesterone. Progesterone inhibits any further ovulation and maintains the lining of the uterus in readiness for the fertilized egg. If the egg is fertilized it travels down the Fallopian tube, embedding itself in the lining of the uterus. The corpus luteum continues to secrete progesterone until about the twelfth week of pregnancy when the *placenta* takes over the task.

If the egg is not fertilized the corpus luteum disappears at about the twenty-fourth day. Secretion of oestrogen and progesterone drops very rapidly between the twenty-fourth and twenty-eighth day, resulting in the breakdown of the uterine lining and the beginning of the menstrual flow. The FSH from the pituitary again becomes dominant and a new follicle and egg begin to develop.

Menstruation

Menstruation is no more than the process in which the unwanted lining of the uterus is passed from the body. Menstrual fluid comes out through the vagina and consists of broken down tissue and some blood. This is the same blood that usually flows in the body except that it does not contain clotting agents. It is the same blood and tissue that would have sustained the egg had it been fertilized. There is nothing especially unclean about this substance although it may develop a slight, unpleasant odour due to further breakdown after leaving the body. Menstruation requires from three to seven days a month, usually four or five, and about a cup of fluid is lost over the period.

First menstruation usually begins between the ages of ten and fourteen, although it may not occur until age seventeen or eighteen years. It is usually preceded or accompanied by enlargement of the breasts and the appearance of public hair.

The menstrual cycle continues to operate for as long as thirty to thirty-five years, during which time it may be interrupted by pregnancy or illness. The cessation of the cycle comes as part of the ageing process. The ageing body normally produces smaller quantities of the hormones which control the cycle, and ultimately it ceases. This time is known as the menopause or 'change of life'.

Ovulation may not occur during the year or so after the first menstruation. Similarly, the cessation of menstruation at menopause does not necessarily mean that ovulation has stopped. Some women remain fertile for a year or two after their last menstruation.

Since there are no hard and fast rules we stress again that physiology is only an outline and must be supplemented by individual body awareness.

Painful menstruation

To be born female is to be born under a curse, or at least it seems so to all those women who suffer the monthly misery of painful periods. This problem has become so widespread over the last few generations that it is now regarded as 'normal' for menstruation to be accompanied by a variety of physical ills and emotional distress. We do hear stories of rare women for whom menstruation is not a burden, we might even know such a woman, but these few are regarded as fortunate to be somehow spared the usual agonies of womanhood. Yet 'normal' is not ideal – it is only an index of what happens to most people, and in acquiescing to the norm we have forgotten that things could be otherwise. Period pain, like any other pain, is a sign that there is something amiss in the body and it will not do to accept this recurrent torment like mere dumb cattle. Through yoga we can take positive action to eliminate period pain and rediscover our womanly heritage of health.

Menstrual difficulty (dysmenorrhoea) spawns as much wretchedness as the common cold, and medical insight into this problem is equally limited. However, one of the few researchers in this field, Dr. Katherina Dalton (USA), has established that 'woman's pain' is not one, but actually two distinct problems.

Spasmodic dysmenorrhoea is characterized by cramps and acute pain in the lower abdomen, with perhaps nausea or shakiness at the beginning of the period. It generally appears in women under twenty-five and usually clears up when the first child is born.

Congestive dysmenorrhoea is associated with the terrible tension that doctors call the 'pre-menstrual syndrome'. A heavy, dull aching in the abdomen and lower back may begin up to three or four days before the bleeding itself. Some women notice swelling and tenderness in the breasts, swollen abdomen or a generally bloated feeling. Greater fluid retention may be reflected in a temporary weight increase of up to three kilos, and there may be some nausea. Headaches, general stiffness and constipation are common. The worst aspects are the irritability, depression and lethargy that make this time of the month so emotionally debilitating. Both the physical and psychic congestion lessen in intensity when bleeding begins, and are relieved when the blood flow is most profuse. This kind of menstrual problem is common to women of all ages from puberty to menopause, and seems to get worse with every pregnancy.

34

Although medical science has not been able to detect beyond doubt the cause of this pain, Dr. Dalton's evidence, and that of Drs. Carey and Pinkerton in Australia, indicated that both spasmodic and congestive dysmenorrhoea are due to hormonal imbalance. With spasmodic pain there is too much progesterone in the body, while congestive problems are due to an excess of oestrogen. Another researcher, Dr. Elizabeth Connel, suggests that uterine cramps could be due to high levels of prostaglandins. These are hormone-like substances produced by the lining of the uterus in great quantities just before it is shed. Lack of progesterone (which indicates an excess of oestrogen) also causes the body cells to retain sodium and lose potassium. This has severe consequences, for the transmission of impulses throughout the nervous system and brain depends on the correct sodium/potassium ratio. It seems then, that hormonal imbalance is also the physiological root of our emotional vulnerability during the menses.

Yogic approach

Doctors usually treat menstrual difficulties with pain relievers and hormonal supplements (birth control pills) and a certain percentage of women on oral contraceptives find their period easier and the flow lighter. However, the pill is, at best, a risky business and increasing numbers of women prefer not to use it. Yoga, on the other hand, offers natural and effective methods without toxic side-effects and with benefits that extend far beyond the physical.

Many women ask if it is safe to perform asanas during their periods. It is essential not to strain at any time, but apart from this usual precaution there is absolutely no reason to abandon your practices. One reporter comments: "A majority of doctors now believe that not only can women participate in any strenuous activity at any time, but that they actually benefit from it. A 1965 study comparing 65 women swimmers with 138 non-athletic students revealed that the swimmers had far less menstrual difficulty."

Sirshasana (headstand) and sarvangasana (shoulder stand) are not advisable during menstruation, but vajrasana, shashankasana, marjariasana and abdominal breathing in shavasana help to relieve cramp. Congestive period pain is relieved when the menstrual flow is at its peak and the flow is quickened by contractions of the uterus such as those in orgasm. This suggests that moola bandha could be particularly beneficial, although you must discontinue this practice at the very first suggestion of faintness or other unpleasant effects.

During the rest of the cycle a balanced program of asanas will harmonize hormone production through their subtle manipulation of the glands. Asanas massage and compress the glands and internal organs, forcing stale blood out and allowing fresh blood to circulate. The glands and the whole reproductive system are toned and strengthened. A good program would include surya namaskara, sarvangasana, halasana, kandharasana, matsyasana, bhujangasana, shalabh-asana, dhanurasana, paschimottanasana, moola bandha and vajroli mudra. Meditation practices, notably yoga nidra and antar mouna, are also ideal for relieving the tension that disturbs our physical and emotional harmony.

Diet

A pure diet of grains and vegetables aids menstrual problems. High protein diets, especially those based on meat, definitely aggravate the problem, and it is interesting to note that the incidence of dysmenorrhoea runs parallel to the increased consumption of meat in affluent countries.

With the trend back to simple, vegetarian food, many women have reported dramatic improvement in period difficulties, with a much lighter blood flow. Even those who still eat meat have reaped notable benefits from cutting down on coffee and processed food, especially sugar, polished rice and white flour products. We should also eat very ripe bananas and fresh orange, or lemon juice around period time, to compensate for the temporary depletion of potassium that is disturbing to the nervous system.

36

Negative attitude

Period pain is not imaginary, it's very real and often there are definite physical reasons for it. Yet in many cases it is exaggerated by negative or unclear emotional attitudes about sexual feelings and sexual activities in general. Too often there is an underlying guilt complex, so that we feel (perhaps unconsciously) that the pain is somehow punishment for sins, real or imagined, in our sexual lives. This misconception so easily arises at puberty when the onset of menstruation coincides with the upsurge of desire.

One Australian study involved young women who reported that they suffered 'very severe' pain and spent one to several days in bed each month as a result. These women were given individual interviews and a series of relaxation sessions using a technique similar to yoga nidra. The therapist would guide them through several rotations of body awareness and then evoke a series of appropriate images to desensitize the subjects' reaction to the pain and to menstruation itself. Results were most successful, with all subjects reporting a reduction in tension, pain and time in bed. Six months later more than half reported that they were still having pain-free periods and they showed an improved attitude to menstruation generally.

In some primitive societies a girl's first menstruation is regarded as the sign of sexual maturity and is celebrated as the coming of womanhood. However, in most cultures it is surrounded by shame and secrecy, if not outright taboo. This attitude, based on ignorance and superstition, is explicit for Moslem, Hindu and Jewish women who must be ritually purified after each period. This makes it difficult for women, especially young girls, to accept the natural functioning of their bodies. Biological facts are often unknown and the taboo on discussion of this subject deepens the mystery. This is a major contributing factor to the 'women's pain' and tension that so often accompanies menstruation.

The great saint Ramakrishna was very fastidious about his food and he strictly adhered to the rules governing the

37

non-acceptance of food prepared or served by someone not of Brahmin caste. He took only *prasad* from the temples or food cooked by his wife, Sarada Devi. However, according to Hindu custom, women may not prepare food while they are menstruating. In his biography of Sarada Devi, Swami Gambhirananda records that Ramakrishna said, "Look here, my dear, my liver trouble has increased because you didn't cook my food during these days. Why didn't you do so?"

The Mother explained, "Women can't cook for anybody during the days of their impurity."

"Who says they can't?" asked the Master. "Do it for me, you won't incur any sin thereby. Would you explain which part of your body is impure – skin, flesh, bone or marrow? Know that purity and impurity reside in the mind; there's nothing impure outside."

After that the Mother always cooked for him. The Master, highly delighted at this said, "See my dear, how healthy is my body by taking your dishes."

The significance of this can only be fully appreciated when we realize that Ramakrishna was always concerned that his wife should set an example for other women by observing all the restrictions relating to Brahmin women, and that even till he died, he would not otherwise bend the caste rules to accept even boiled rice from anyone who was not a Brahmin.

Menstruation is brought up in arguments concerning the fitness of women in general, and particularly their fitness to undertake employment outside the home. It is widely believed that women are less competent at this time, more susceptible to accident and insanity. (In the face of such attitudes, it's no wonder that some women even regard menstruation and its pains as the curse of womanhood.) It has also been suggested that pre-menstrual mood changes might seriously affect a woman's intellectual abilities. To examine this question, Sharon Golub of the College of New Rochelle (USA) administered a variety of tests to fifty middle-aged mothers during the week before their period. The women reported that they were more anxious and depressed than normal and that they were experiencing difficulty in concentrating and working efficiently. However, their test performance showed no sign that they were in any way intellectually handicapped prior to menstruation.

This result suggests that women are more the victims of their own negative attitudes about themselves and their bodies than the victims of biological events.

A hint from the past

In India it used to be the custom, and in orthodox Brahmin families it still is, for the women of the household to isolate themselves during the menses. They do not go into the kitchen or puja room, nor do they touch any member of the family. Traditionally, one room is set aside for them and they retire to this room for at least three days. During seclusion the menstruating woman does her own washing and cleaning, and sleeps on a woollen blanket on the floor. She puts aside her sari and covers herself with a single cloth, and if the children must come to her they do so naked. On the fourth day the house is purified by ritual sprinkling with holy water from the Ganga or some other sacred river, the woman bathes, washes her hair and comes out of retreat. The next day she worships in the temple and after this she returns to the kitchen and her husband.

Unfortunately, the origins of this custom have been forgotten and it has been misinterpreted as indicating that women are defiled, impure and polluted during menstruation. In fact, it was not to protect the family from the menstruating woman that these arrangements were made, but to protect the woman from her family.

This period of seclusion provided women with an opportunity to take a break from household duties which, in a traditional family of up to fifty members, were frequently quite arduous. (Many a modern mother wishes she could have time to herself away from housework and children for a few days every month.) This retreat was a psychological protection at a time of heightened emotional sensitivity. Instead of aggravating any irritability or depression, which so easily flare into angry scenes or harsh words, a woman withdrew into the soothing quiet of her room, preserving her peace of mind and family harmony.

These days, women no longer take such elaborate precautions, and old customs are being abandoned as no longer practical. Despite the handicap of discomfort and tension, women have shown themselves quite capable of pursuing their usual interests or careers. Many find that this gives them a satisfaction that cancels out pain altogether. Certainly investigators are showing that women are no more handicapped at this time than men who are having a painful time with high blood pressure or peptic ulcers.

Just the same, an understanding of the rationale behind old customs shatters the misogynist myth of female impurity, and that in itself releases us from shame and much emotional distress. Even though a period of retreat is a luxury few can afford now, we can rearrange our schedules to allow for more rest and privacy if we so desire. Even just an extra hour or so to practise antar mouna can provide the opportunity to relax and get a new perspective on things.

We must remember that the problems which get us down at period time are the same ones that are always with us, only we usually push them aside to get through the day. Our increased sensitivity during menstruation makes us more aware of them, and if we take time off to examine them thoroughly, we may perhaps find a real solution. In antar mouna we simply sit quietly and watch our thoughts and feelings as they pass across the psychic screen behind our closed eyes. Provided we maintain the objective attitude of a witness, and do not judge, this practice is enormously refreshing. On the screen of chidakasha there is nothing good and nothing bad. What we see there is an expression of our unconscious mind, which manifests itself to us in brilliant colours and images that are as entertaining as any surrealist movie, but far more revealing of life's true meaning. Antar

40

mouna provides us with a psychological clear space, and allows us to get in touch with ourselves by acknowledging the parts of our being we often ignore. Just as our body is casting off substances it doesn't need anymore, so we too can throw off worn out ideas and self-images and make the most of this opportunity for self renewal.

The earth has her seasons when autumn leaves fall, while vital sap is withdrawn before its vigorous resurgence in spring time. By adopting a positive attitude to this most natural of womanly processes, we can use full awareness of menstruation and its implications to experience our bond with Mother Earth and join in the rhythms of the cosmos.

Menarche and Menopause

When a natural event coincides with ripened awareness we are opened to new experiences. These are nature's spontaneous initiations, new beginnings, that form the basis of our maturity and wisdom. All cultures and societies recognize the threshold of physical maturity as a time of transition and changing awareness. In many traditions, puberty is marked by special ceremonies that consecrate physical adulthood and awaken the life of the soul. This is the time when girls should be introduced to the practices of yoga. Yogic practices aid towards maintaining health and emotional stability, and also provide the cornerstone of spiritual experience.

Menarche

Puberty is the time a girl becomes sexually mature, capable of bearing children. It is also a process of growth that takes several months, or even more than a year, but which seems subjectively to be a very sudden occurrence. In girls, the first sign of approaching puberty is usually the development of breasts, although this may often be preceded by the appearance of pubic hair. The menarche, or first menstruation, is the climax of this natural process, marking the girl's physical maturity. It also marks the beginning of her final growth into social adulthood.

A celebration

In many traditional cultures, puberty for both boys and girls is surrounded by many symbolic rites. Among certain Australian aborigines the young girl used to be buried up to her waist in warm sand to assist the first flow, and she was fed and cared for by her mother in a sacred place. Later she returned to the tribal camp to celebrate the feast marking her entry into womanhood.

In some parts of India, *kumaripuja* was, and is, celebrated at the time of first menstruation. On the first day, having attained womanhood, the girl is worshipped by family and friends as the incarnation of the maidenly aspect of Shakti – Kumari, symbol of purity and promise. Kumari later grows into Parvati who becomes the consort of Shiva. The kumari is showered with gifts and flowers, and is presented with her first sari. Sometimes there is a festival procession and celebration feast. On the fourth day, after a ritual bath, she goes to the temple to perform puja and from then on takès part in the fasting and other religious observances practised by devout Hindu women.

A time for openness

Such rituals ease what could be a difficult transition, and publicly recognize the young adult's new status. However, many cultures no longer celebrate such ceremonies, and some girls even come to their first menstruation totally unprepared. It is far preferable that girls be able to talk to their mothers about the events occurring in their bodies at this time, for they should become aware of what these processes are, and that they are not harmful but normal. This time is a challenge to both mother and daughter, and provides the opportunity to strengthen the foundations of a warm woman to woman relationship in later years.

Here in India especially, a mother might be shy in discussing such matters, but sensitivity and frank discussion will be appreciated by her daughter. Should a mother feel that her knowledge is inadequate, this is the time to brush up on biological facts. It is also a time for re-evaluating her own attitudes, for negativity is not only detrimental to herself but is easily sensed by her daughter, and will give an unfortunate start to the young girl's experience.

Metamorphosis

Adolescence is characterized by the stresses and strains accompanying periods of rapid personal growth. The physical changes set in motion at puberty continue, and it takes some years for the hormonal balance to assert itself. In these first years, periods are often irregular or painful. Teenage girls may become overweight, their complexions are often blotchy and pimply. The lithe and agile little girl becomes clumsy and awkward while she adjusts to her new body.

Not only does her body become a stranger, but the adolescent girl becomes aware of new roles and responsibilities that often create emotional conflict. At this time she has to recognize her sexual drive and learn how to deal with it. She is certainly denied the expression of these feelings, and in many situations other people will deny that she has them at all. Girls may also have a problem when they notice that men are now sexually aware of them. Some find this natural and even ego-boosting, but many experience being a 'thing' instead of a person, and take some time to develop ways of coping with this depersonalization. In orthodox societies girls are so 'protected' and warned against mixing with boys, or even talking to them, that they are filled with an unnatural fear which only increases their alienation.

During adolescence a girl is under increasing pressure to prepare for marriage and motherhood and she finds she has to abandon a lot of the freedoms of her childhood. Behaviour that was permitted to little girls is no longer appropriate to the young lady who must channel her energies into a more modest demeanour. At this age, girls are more aware of the mass image of femininity – sweet, loving, retiring and, above all, beautiful. Most of them accept this model and try to mould themselves to it, but they are distressed when they

44

can't match up. Adolescent girls typically spend a lot of time fussing over their appearance and brooding over their confusing emotions.

This is a time when a girl must make some compromise between her own ambivalent desires, and restraints and skills she must develop to become a member of adult society. As a result, the sunny little girl often becomes moody and resentful, angry, defiant or sulky, or all these things in turn. To a greater or lesser degree, she may begin to act in ways that are either antisocial or self-destructive. Problems she might have had since early childhood become worse, and her distress and conflict may manifest themselves in irritability, nightmares, bed-wetting, giggling, nail biting, lying, shyness, brooding, sensitiveness or weeping.

Sometimes a girl's behaviour is affected so much that her family thinks she is mentally disturbed. Often parents and family elders do not understand what is happening to the girl, for they are not aware of the relationship between the changes in her body and those in her mind. In such cases an already distressed young woman may be sent to a psychiatrist or mental hospital, where tranquilizers may block the symptoms but do not help her to any greater insight or acceptance. In India pujas are performed, magic and mantras invoked, but all to no use.

Of course, the situation is not so grim for everyone, nor is it unrelieved misery. However, most girls will experience these ups and downs over a period of years. The very intensity of feeling during this phase makes it seem so much worse.

A mother's gift

It goes without saying that this is also a difficult time for mothers with adolescent daughters. Usually at this time a girl will turn to her mother, although fathers have a lot to offer too, and it is precisely at this time that parents can give their child much needed support. A certain detachment is necessary and an ability to allow one's daughter freedom to experiment and explore, while watching at a distance.

45

By introducing her to yoga, a generous mother is making a gift to her daughter of the courage and optimism needed on the path to her own unique destination. The poet Kahlil Gibran has said:

> *Your children are not our children,*
> *They are the sons and daughters of*
> *Life's longing for itself.*
> *They come through you but not from you,*
> *And though they are with you*
> *They belong not to you.*

Diksha

In India it was a custom, now long gone, to send girls to an ashram for gurukul education, just as is still done for boys. The Sanskrit classic, *Abhigyana Shakuntalam* informs us that young girls were educated in the ashram for a full twelve years. Girls were also initiated into upanayanam. In that era girls as well as boys received this diksha, together with instruction in surya namaskara, pranayama and Gayatri mantra. In other religions, this diksha is paralleled by the sacrament of confirmation among Christians, the navzote among Parsis, and bar mitzvah among Jews – all of which are conferred equally upon girls as well as boys.

At this time, when a girl's life is opening before her and new possibilities are coming into view, a sensitive mother is in the position to foster her daughter's discrimination by introducing her to yoga. Yoga practices have beneficial effects on the whole constitution, regulating the organic functions and balancing the hormones. Asanas, especially surya namaskara, will regulate the periods, control weight, clear the complexion and safely release aggressive energy. Pranayama and japa will bring relaxation, soothe the emotions and assist in developing a positive self-awareness to counteract morbid self-consciousness. Yoga practices can help establish emotional stability and give a young girl confidence and poise she would otherwise lack.

More importantly, yoga practices will preserve the special link that children have with their inner world, ensuring that during the transition to adulthood this awareness is not destroyed, but transmuted into a mature spirituality.

Change of life

The Vedas speak of four ashrama or stages of life outlining the usual course of social and spiritual life. The first of these is brahmacharya ashrama, governing the conduct of young people before marriage. At first they were subject to parents and family and then young men and women left home and went to live with and serve their guru. During this time they furthered their education, with an emphasis on spiritual development that prepared them for future duties.

Marriage marked the beginning of grihastha ashrama where spiritual growth is stimulated by raising a family and taking an active role in society. Once the children were grown, and a couple had discharged their responsibilities, they entered vanaprastha ashrama, withdrawing from society to develop their formal spiritual practices. After a lifetime's experience, they renounced the world for sannyasa ashrama.

Initiation into upanayanam at puberty marks the beginning of brahmacharya ashram, and vanaprastha diksha in middle age marks the transition from a full householder life to one of more intense sadhana. For many women, the physical fact of menopause crystallizes a 'change of life' that is more than merely biological. While vanaprashtha ashrama does not necessarily depend on menopause, this natural ripening does stimulate women to a re-evaluation of their social role and spiritual life that heralds a new era in the growth of the soul.

Menopause

As part of the natural ageing process, the body produces smaller and smaller quantities of reproductive hormones. The ovaries and uterus shrink, and ultimately the menstrual cycle ceases. This point is called menopause or the climacteric.

Like puberty, menopause is a gradual process that may extend over several years. Usually it occurs between forty-five and fifty-five, although it has been known to start earlier. In cold countries women who begin menstruation earlier usually experience menopause later. In hot countries, both menarche and menopause tend to occur a little earlier. Other factors affecting the age of climacteric seem to be one's general standard of nutrition, weight, and whether or not one has had children.

An early menopause can occur as a result of disease or surgical removal of the ovaries. Removal of the uterus (hysterectomy) usually does not precipitate menopause unless both ovaries are also removed. The modern practice is to leave at least one ovary (if healthy) which continues to produce sufficient oestrogen to delay menopause until the usual age.

The decline of oestrogen and progesterone triggers minor changes in the bones, skin and circulatory system, but essentially all the menopause really signifies is that a woman can no longer conceive a child. All other faculties and capacities remain intact, and there is definitely no halt to continuing personal development.

Physical symptoms

The gradual decline in hormonal production begins years before menstruation ceases, but as decrease continues, the menstrual flow becomes lighter, shorter and more widely spaced. Some months there will be no flow at all. In some women, after long gaps, the period may occasionally be heavy and profuse, but in others the cycle stops more abruptly. Among a small percentage of women (some say around fifteen percent) the cycle resumes briefly after a year or more of complete absence, but then it stops altogether.

As the body adjusts to the rapidly changing chemical balance some physical discomfort is usually experienced. This is not just psychological, but has a definite physical basis, and is felt even by some women who in all ways are healthy, active and positive.

Hot flushes are sudden surges of heat in the chest, upper back, throat and head, sometimes accompanied by patchy redness in the skin. When caught in one of these heat waves you perspire profusely, and afterwards may feel chilly and weak. Hot flushes usually last a minute or two, but in severe cases may continue for up to fifteen minutes. They are unpredictable, and may occur several times a day. Some women find that flushing occurs on the days that would have marked the beginning of their periods.

Hot flushes come mostly at night ('night sweats') and they are often so heavy that they drench sheets and bedding. Since they disturb one's sleep, they could be a major cause of fatigue and irritability during the day. Hot flushes are not completely understood, but seem to be an attempt of the hypothalamus to cope with sudden hormonal changes. Once the body adjusts to a lower oestrogen level, they stop.

Vaginal atrophy is the medical term for dryness and loss of elasticity in the vagina, resulting from greatly reduced secretions of the vaginal walls. Vaginal dryness can make intercourse painful, and leave you more vulnerable to infection. It occurs usually during the later part of menopause and severe cases usually do not develop until five to ten years after menstruation has ended.

Weight gain is not a necessary outcome of menopause, but at this time the appetite is disrupted and may increase. On the other hand, as we get older the body's actual need for food decreases. A regular yogic diet and attention to the inner intelligence of the body will prevent overweight.

Menopausal syndrome is a term coined by doctors to cover not only those problems just mentioned, but also a range of other symptoms that include headaches, digestive upset, dizzy spells, palpitations, blood pressure irregularities, insomnia, lethargy, irritability and depression. These problems are not directly linked to the fall in oestrogen levels. However, the stress of hormonal fluctuations definitely influences a woman's mood and these difficulties could then be precipitated in more vulnerable women.

A minority

The presence of any of these physical or emotional difficulties varies from day to day, and some women do not experience them at all. Studies in England and America indicate that only hot flushes, night sweats and vaginal atrophy are directly related to the climacteric. In general, it seems that most women (nine out of ten) will experience some sort of discomfort, but usually not to a degree that disrupts their lives or requires medical treatment. It is only a minority of women (two out of ten) who experience a wider range of problems, or who find them so severe as to disrupt normal living.

Therapies

- *Hormonal replacement therapy* is given by doctors in severe cases of menopausal disturbance, and consists of taking repeated doses of synthetic oestrogen. Although often effective, it is controversial because it is implicated in higher risks of endometrial cancer, hypertension, blood clots and heart disease.
- *Homeopathy* is an excellent aid, especially in conjunction with yoga sadhana. Sepia is commonly effective for depression and pulsatilla for hot flushes.
- *Proper diet* can help minimize menopausal and post-menopausal difficulties. Calcium deficiency sometimes results from the lack of ovarian hormones, and should be compensated by extra calcium (milk and green vegetables) and vitamin D (sunshine). These will keep bones strong and avoid osteoporosis. Shortage of certain proteins (notably tryptophan) is implicated in depression, and may be exaggerated by oestrogen deficiency. A slight increase in proteins will be helpful to avert depression from this cause, so your diet should include milk, dal, soya beans, peanuts, wheat, rice and other grains.
- *Regular yoga practice* from the twenties and thirties will ensure maximum health of all body systems. When menopause occurs, the kidneys, bowels and lungs are adequately prepared to withstand chemical changes.

Negative attitudes

In earlier times the change of life was more distressing because of its veil of superstition and confusion, and it was believed to involve a complete loss of femininity: a woman's juices dried up and left her nothing but a wrinkled old crone. Although today's increased knowledge has mostly banished that attitude, it is still the basis for the anxieties and fears which beset women at this time. These additional sufferings are very real, but they are not physically determined. It has been observed that women who have always followed a discipline of self culture, in addition to their family involvements, generally have fewer regrets and misgivings at this time. Women whose approach to the change is sensible and positive are less susceptible to psychological distress and depression.

Studies by Pauline Bart, Bernice Neugarten and the Boston Women's Health Collective show that many of the miseries of menopause are not necessarily experienced at all by many women in that stage of life. These researches have found that direct signs of menopause (hot flushes, vaginal atrophy) are found amongst menopausal women, even those who are optimistic and active. However, depression, insomnia, headache and other symptoms of the 'menopausal syndrome' are actually reported more often by women in the twenty-five to forty years age group. It would seem then, that these problems are not specific to the menopause, but are a reflection of women's ongoing dissatisfaction throughout their adult lives. These problems and dissatisfactions are not necessarily caused by menopause, but simply brought to the forefront at that time.

Misplaced fears

Generally speaking, it is younger women who are most negative in their attitudes to the change of life. With this experience yet before them, they have very distorted ideas on the matter, and tend to anticipate that it will be much worse than it is. Women who have actually been through menopause are often less negative about it. They seem to have a better perspective, and find menopause less significant in the overall context of their personal growth and fulfilment. This would indicate that younger women and older women should get together and talk to each other more frankly about these things.

One central area of fear and doubt is that a women's sensual desire will be extinguished by menopause. Speaking to older women, we find it is not unusual for older women to continue an active married life well after menopause. Contrary to the old crone myth, it is not uncommon for forward-looking women to experience a reflowering of intimacy with their husbands, and a resurgence of other interests and talents.

Another fear is that menopause is the beginning of the end – a rapid descent into senility. Around 1900, that is within the era of our grandmothers and great-grandmothers, life expectancy in most countries was much less than it is today. In America for instance, in 1900 a woman could expect to live an average of fifty years, and her menopause came around forty. These days, the menopause occurs around the same time or a little later, and yet the average woman can expect to live into her seventies. Similar increase can be seen throughout the world.

So, we can see that menopause is hardly the end of a woman's active life. There is still nearly a full one third of our lives before us, and in these prime years we have the advantage of so much earlier experience and many fewer duties and distractions.

Yogic outlook

For women who have been practising yoga in earlier years, physical difficulties at menopause are less intense and any emotional disturbances practically non-existent. As with all hormonal imbalances, yogasanas have a tremendous stabilizing effect. Some oestrogen continues to be produced by the liver and kidneys even after the ovaries cease their secretions, and the correct yoga practices can stimulate these extra sources as partial compensation for loss of ovarian hormones. Even if you have not been practising yoga before, it is never too late to begin, and women who have undergone a hysterectomy, or any other major operations, are equally able to commence.

The practice of inverted asanas like vipareeta karani asana, sarvangasana, sirshasana are all helpful, especially in conjunction with backward bending asanas. Pranayama, highly esteemed by many women at this time, can help compensate for irritability and loss of sleep. Most valuable are the mudras and bandhas – moola bandha, jalandhara bandha and uddiyana bandha – together with various meditation practices.

On one hand, meditation practices provide a means of confronting fears and anxieties that might accentuate physical distress. They also give the clarity and inspiration to make most fruitful use of the years ahead. On the other hand, many older women find themselves very capable and sensitive to meditation practices at this time of life. They have lived out many of their ambitions and find that their attachments are naturally fading, so that there are fewer distractions when they practise meditation.

Karma sannyasa

In vedic times, husband and wife used to retire (literally) to the forest, and gracefully entered the stage of life called vanaprastha ashrama. These days it is not practical, or even possible, for most people to do this, however many women do emerge from their change of life with an altered sense of priorities, a new sense of values which gives prominence to their inner life.

The initiation that strengthens and nourishes this new awareness is called vanaprastha diksha or karma sannyasa. This diksha and our yoga sadhana do not encourage us to retire from the world, but to live in it with a different philosophy, and a wider deeper awareness.

53

In order to complete our lives, round out a full life, and fulfil our essential goal in living we must experience flowering in the realm of awareness, which can be brought about by vichara, dhyana and other sadhanas. Without this higher experience, without atma anubhuti, our lives come to an end with us still incomplete, still grasping for a meaning in having lived. Karma sannyasa provides us with a framework that draws together the lessons of all our previous experience, and provides us with a sadhana to bring our spiritual life to maturity in serenity and true wisdom.

Growing into Womanhood

Every society assigns different personality characteristics to men and to women. Men are supposed to be 'masculine', women are supposed to be 'feminine', and each is supposed to be the opposite of the other. That a human being with a male body should exhibit a masculine personality, that a human being with a female body should have a feminine personality – this is taken for granted. It is assumed (mostly unconsciously) that masculine and feminine behaviour is inborn, that reproductive role determines personality.

Women are traditionally seen as affectionate, gentle, understanding, sensitive, easily influenced and unaggressive. They are seen as adapting to others rather than trying to dominate them, as non-competitive and self-effacing. Women are regarded as feeling creatures rather than thinking humans; inner-directed rather than outwardly striving. They are not seen as strong, independent, ambitious, or self-assertive – all of these qualities are associated with the masculine personality. This image, or ideal model of feminine make up is so widely held, regardless of evidence to the contrary, that it has come to be the stereotype against which all women are measured.

So much in common
Studies by endocrinologists into the effects of hormones on personality indicate that specifically male and specifically female hormones can have a slight and subtle influence on

the personality. High levels of the male hormone testosterone seem to be linked with more aggressive personalities, and could be a biological basis for the observation that men are generally more aggressive than women, whereas the female hormone oestrogen, seems to have a 'feminizing' influence. However, even these researchers insist that hormonal levels can do nothing more than create a conducive background to the development of certain potential patterns of personality. They perhaps establish a slight predisposition, but this is still very much secondary to the environment in which one grows up, and the opportunities for expression inherent in the culture.

The most arresting finding in these personality studies is that the differences between any two women or any two men are far greater than the difference between any given man and woman. The difference between the highest and lowest test scores for women, and the highest and lowest scores for men – these differences are far greater than the differences between the average man and the average woman. Certain differences between men and women are undeniable, but these are practically insignificant in relation to the vast possibilities open to both sexes.

That a man acts like a man and that a woman behaves as a woman has come to seem a biological fact – right, natural and unalterable, the permanent expression of deepest human nature. It is not a biological fact, but a social artifact. The manly man and the womanly woman are the products of a long process of socialization, that subtle educational process that moulds a new-born individual into a human, social being. This immense task is performed by the child's family, friends, peers and the wider community (through the various types of media). Not only does the child develop as an individual, but he or she is also moulded a fit member of society. This comprehensive education is continuously carried on in a million small ways, night and day, for years. It permeates every fibre that makes up the pattern and texture of one's life.

Social process

While growing up in a female body one is treated as a female by men and women, and this is different from the way males are treated by other men and by women. Almost imperceptibly one learns what it means to be a woman among women and a woman among men.

The difference in the way people treat men and women begins in infancy. Mothers and nurses pick up girls with smaller gestures; they do not move them as far or as rapidly, and they use higher tones of voice than they do with baby boys. They touch girls more gently. On the other hand, baby boys are picked up with large sweeping gestures and touched a little more roughly. People speak more loudly to them. This is based on the assumption that boys are stronger and that girls need more protection, an assumption that is conveyed to the child through this and many other, apparently insignificant, experiences.

People are not just reacting to a male or female baby-doll, they are interacting with a potential man or woman, and more or less unconsciously playing a part in forming the child's future personality.

As children grow older each sex is subjected to its own system of approved rewards and encouragements. Running, jumping, climbing and rough play are pastimes of little boys the world over, pastimes from which girls are usually discouraged because they might injure themselves or develop undesirable toughness. Girls are restricted more to the immediate household and encouraged to involve themselves in quiet games. They are most often directed into verbal or manipulative games, and are generally restrained to physically passive activities. Playing with dolls or younger children is universal for girls and they are frequently taught early to amuse themselves with needle and thread. Later on in life a woman's cleverness with her hands, attention to the small details of any activity and similar traits are regarded as inborn, for this early training is overlooked or dismissed as 'just playing'.

Girls are generally regarded as needing more protective upbringing, which is to say that they are more carefully and constantly supervised, and spend more of their time with adults. This probably accounts for the observation that little girls are more 'grown up' than little boys of the same age. This praise of a girl's maturity is often also a measure of her passivity. While a certain amount of assertiveness and disobedience is tolerated in boys as a sign of their independence, it is heavily frowned upon in girls who are praised for being more 'sensible', that is, more submissive to parental (social) demands and expectations.

In view of this training, it is easy to understand the psychologists' finding that girls acquire a longer attention span earlier in life than boys, that they learn to sit still earlier than boys. Until puberty, girls show a greater ease in expressing themselves through words than boys do. Although the boys catch up, girls resort to words more often. Whereas boys might give anger or hostility physical expression, girls are more likely to do it through words. Thus women earn the reputation for being unaggressive, but this is not really the case. They have only learned a different manner of expression. Women can be just as aggressive, assertive, independent, ruthless or strong as men can, but their ways of expressing these characteristics are different from those of men.

Just how effective this subliminal childhood training is, and how early it becomes established, are indicated by studies with American school children. Although American children might, perhaps, be more quickly socialized by the greater input from radio, TV and comics, this would not limit these findings only to American children, or even western children, for they point out the trend operating in all societies. Researchers took three groups of school children aged five, nine and fourteen years old and measurements were made of their attitudes to male and female roles in relation to the family, society and emotional characteristics. Children with working mothers, or from different social classes and racial backgrounds all held similar views within their age groups.

Researchers found that even five year olds held highly stereotyped views, regardless of background. The nine year olds were the most open of the three groups, but even they assigned social and emotional roles to both men and women according to the prevailing social images of masculinity and femininity. The fourteen year olds were the most strongly stereotyped, believing that inter-personal and emotional qualities were essential for women but not for men. Whereas younger children were more willing to favour women working outside the family, only the girls in the fourteen years group supported this idea. The boys in this group were the least flexible concerning role expansion, rejecting the idea of working women almost unanimously.

This study shows us the extent to which children have absorbed social attitudes on the appropriate behaviour and activities of each sex. Such uncritical acceptance of the limitations of these stereotypes has a limiting effect on children's images of themselves and the possibilities they believe life holds open to them.

The means of conveying this knowledge are apparently so trivial, so commonplace, that they are accepted as natural or overlooked altogether. People cease to be aware that the resulting 'feminine' or 'masculine' personality is the outcome of a social game; that the conventions and limits are not natural boundaries but ones agreed upon by society, and are therefore changeable according to the needs of society and the individuals of whom, and for whom, society exists.

Across cultures

Girls in western countries are allowed a great deal of freedom when compared with their sisters in southern Europe or the Orient. Young girls of seventeen to twenty-five might be working and living away from their parents, for instance, whereas in Greece or India girls can only leave the house with a chaperone. Western girls are, therefore, comparatively more independent, assertive and confident, and might seem rather bold and unfeminine when they find themselves in more restricted societies. On the other hand, girls from more traditional societies may seem overly fearful, inhibited and colourless by comparison. It is not some biological freak that women can have these qualities, it is just a result of their upbringing in a culture which has different values.

Anthropologists have found that there are no innate male or female characteristics after studying various primitive societies. These societies are called 'primitive' because their patterns of living are closer to nature. They are, therefore, closer to whatever may be innate to humankind in its natural state. As a people becomes increasingly 'civilized' its patterns of living are altered so that the fundamentals are filtered through deeper and deeper layers of learning and culture. Thus, primitive peoples, whose lifestyles may have been unchanged for thousands of years, are ideal subjects for investigating the innate basis of our humanity.

Studies such as Margaret Mead's *Sex and Temperament* have demonstrated that there are no innate male or female temperaments. Studying three New Guinea societies, she discovered that in one, the Arapesh, women did indeed exhibit the temperamental traits of passivity, tenderness and unaggressiveness that are associated with the innately feminine. On the other hand, so did the men. In a neighbouring tribe, the Mundugumor, the males exhibited the traits of egotism, boldness and aggression that have long been associated with the innately masculine. So, however, did the women. In the third society, the Tchambuli, the 'masculine' traits were exhibited by the women and the 'feminine' traits by the men. Dr. Mead drew the obvious conclusion: "Standardized personality differences between the sexes...are cultural creations to which each generation, male and female, is trained to conform."

Synthesis

Stereotypes fit no-one exactly. Yet they do exist and they exert an influence because they are believed most of the time by large numbers of people. Social images of masculinity and femininity are the standard against which individual men and women measure themselves, and to which they are encouraged to conform. To examine these stereotypes is not to get involved in the 'battle of the sexes' and futile arguments over which one is 'better'. It is simply to see what we are and what we are not, so that we can see what we might become.

There have been several psychological tests devised to measure the degree of 'masculinity' or 'femininity' present in one's personality. That is, these tests measure how closely one's personality fits the accepted stereotype for one's sex. Studies conducted with these test-devices have amassed considerable evidence that closely following traditional sex-patterns is not consistent with optimum mental health. For example, women who have high femininity scores (that is, who closely fit the mass feminine ideal) also exhibit high anxiety, low self-esteem and low self-acceptance, which is the jargon for saying they are nervous, lack self-confidence and are very dissatisfied with themselves. Men who conform closely to the masculine ideal have less trouble adjusting during adolescence, but exhibit the same symptoms later on; they are anxious, highly neurotic and very dissatisfied with themselves.

Furthermore, greater intellectual development is consistently related to higher masculinity ratings in girls and higher femininity scores in boys. It has been seen that boys with more 'feminine' traits and girls with more 'masculine' traits tend to be more intelligent than their fellows. Boys who are strongly masculine and girls who strongly feminine tend to have lower overall intelligence scores, lower spatial ability and show less creativity.

Because people learn during their formative years to suppress any behaviour that might be considered undesirable or inappropriate for their sex, it would seem obvious that sex-typing restricts behaviour. Various psychological studies have found this to be the case.

In one study men with high masculinity scores (that is, highly stereotyped masculine behaviour) did masculine things very well, but did not do feminine things. They were independent and assertive when necessary, but lacked the ability to express warmth, playfulness and concern: important, if traditionally feminine traits. Similarly, women were restricted in their ability to express masculine characteristics. For instance, they were not independent in judgement or assertive of their own preferences.

These researchers use the term *androgynous* (andro: male, gyne: female) for those people who do not closely fit the stereotype for their sex, but show a mixture of both feminine and masculine characteristics. They found that androgynous people were not limited by labels in feeling or behaviour. In contrast to strongly sex-typed people, androgynous men and women did equally well in both masculine and feminine activities. They could be independent and assertive when they needed to be, and warm and responsive in the appropriate situations.

Removing the burden of stereotype allows people to express freely the best traits of both men and women. Freeing people from rigid sex-roles and allowing them to be androgynous should make them more flexible in meeting new situations, and less restricted in what they can do and how they express themselves. In modern society an adult sometimes has to be assertive, independent and self-reliant but traditional femininity makes many women unable to behave in this way. On the other hand, we must be able to relate to other people, to be sensitive to their needs and concerned about their welfare, to give and receive emotional support. Adherence to traditional masculinity keeps men from responding in such supposedly feminine ways.

Androgyny, by sharp contrast, encourages every individual to be both independent and tender, assertive and yielding, masculine and feminine as the situation demands. Freedom from stereotypes greatly expands the range of behaviour open to everyone, thus enabling people to cope more efficiently with diverse situations. The most effective and happy individuals are those who have developed both the masculine and the feminine sides of themselves, for to deny is to mutilate or deform.

Yoga emphasizes that we must break the dominance of the ego and reduce it to its proper functioning. One way in which the ego manifests is the sex-stereotype. Through recognition of this stereotype we can know just how much our behaviour is socially determined and how much is our true nature (swabhava). While we must learn to know our limitations, there is no need to add to them. Once we can see through socially imposed limits, we can examine and perhaps transcend those of a more personal kind. The popular ideals of masculinity and femininity are useful here in pointing out our deficiencies, showing us what strengths we need to develop in order to become whole.

Transcendence

In meditation we discover and decipher the unconscious symbols that influence our view of ourselves and others. Among these symbols a woman will find her dominant image of the ideal man. On one level this image is simply a personification of erotic desire, but it is also a link between the conscious and the unconscious. This masculine ideal is a complement to a woman's personality, a manifestation of the masculine elements in her make-up. In recognizing and accepting the symbol she can pass through to a realm of feeling that enriches her way of experiencing the world. This puts a woman more directly in touch with a side of her inner nature that is no longer hidden but is meaningfully integrated into her consciousness, taking her closer to the goal of wholeness.

Integration of the male and female elements of the personality is symbolized in India by the androgynous deity Ardhanareeshwara. The statues and carvings of this deity are half male, half female: Shiva on the right, Shakti on the left. This deity embodies the ancient truth that divinity is neither male nor female, but a transcendental fusion of the two. In each of us Ardhanareeshwara is represented by the nadis ida

63

and pingala. These are the two major currents of prana that flow on either side of the spine: ida to the left, and pingala to the right. These nadis determine both the constitution of the body, and the character of the mind and emotions. In traditional descriptions ida is regarded as the feminine potential and pingala as the masculine, but both are present in every human being, man and woman alike.

The descriptions 'feminine' and 'masculine' were applied by the ancients in their widest and most positive sense, as key words or abbreviations for many further qualities and associations. When the majority of our energy circulates in one or the other of these channels, it activates a particular mode of perceiving and acting, an entire way of 'being' in the world.

All the ancient cultures recognized these twin foundations of the soul. In Alchemy ida and pingala are pictured as sun and moon, or the lion and the deer. In the cards of the Tarot they appear on several cards as two pillars on the right and left borders. In Chinese philosophy ida and pingala correspond to yin and yang. Today, science is giving attention to these potentials through its research on the right and left hemispheres of the brain.

Rather than think of masculine and feminine, we could regard these forces as the way of receptivity and the way of initiative. Ida represents the receptivity that keeps us open to see many new possibilities both from without and within. Pingala represents our initiative, creative action, our ability to express and shape possibilities in the world. We could say that the way of being we experience under the influence of ida nadi gives us the *inspiration* for action, and pingala nadi brings into being our capacity for creative *expression*.

The task for any yoga sadhaka is to understand how these forces wax and wane, how they compliment and compensate for each other. When ida and pingala are in perfect balance, when we discover and accept both influences, then sushumna nadi awakens – the path and potential for transcendence. The hatha yoga texts tell us to go beyond,

beyond the sun (pingala) and the moon (ida). This is the realm of the transcendental personality that is the flowering of our true humanity.

Aspects of Ida	Aspects of Pingala
moon	sun
night	day
blue	red
cool	hot
negative	positive
mind	vitality
manas	prana
subjective	objective
wholistic	sequential
artistic	practical
colour, space, sound	words
inward looking	outward looking
intuition	logic

Primal Energy

In the yogic experience energy is all, for energy interplay is the cosmic law. The whole universe is a vivid reality spun from the interplay of energy and consciousness, the loving *lila*, play of Shiva and Shakti. To the yogi, it is not the physical body that matters, but the quality and quantity of the energy that mobilizes the body, motivates the mind and elevates consciousness.

Primal energy

Kundalini is that aspect of universal life force (prana) that specifically animates human beings. Man's primal energy is kundalini shakti, which has its highest expression in spiritual enlightenment, but finds its gross and immediate manifestation in sexual energy. This primal energy is the explosive power in man; all that we call personal magnetism, charisma. Most people do not yet recognize what western psychology has rediscovered and tantra has known all along – that this primal energy is the motivating force of all human emotion and activity.

Energy is polarized; it can attract or repel; it is positive or negative. We can see this most readily in relation to magnets with their north and south poles, or electricity with its positive and negative terminals. This is the pattern of existence, the spontaneous play of Shiva and Shakti, consciousness and energy. Creation of life, energy and matter is not possible unless these positive and negative forces unite. The human counterpart to the universal evolution of Shiva/Shakti is found in the play of the male and female in various social and personal relationships.

Freud maintained that this energy is stored in the unconscious mind and seeks conscious expression in the form of instinctual desires. Freud called these instinctive impulses "drives" (encompassing both their dynamic and motivating aspects). Yogis call them *vasana*. Our emotions, the feelings we have about these drives, are dependent on their satisfaction or frustration.

The demands of survival and social coexistence, not to mention spiritual evolution, means that we cannot give free rein to our desires. Yet this primal energy is imperious and does not readily tolerate frustration. If desire is denied expression for any reason, the energy behind it is deflected back into the unconscious mind where it is rechannelled for expression in different ways. A woman may redirect this energy constructively into work, creative and spiritual understandings. On the other hand this primal energy may find negative emotional expression as aggression, anxiety or some form of inner tension.

If the frustration of desire is accompanied by a particularly painful experience, both the desire and the memory of the experience are pushed deep into the unconscious mind where a great deal of energy is spent in keeping them beyond remembrance. Such a scar on the mind is known in yoga as a samskara, and it is regarded as a major obstacle to full spiritual realization. Although we are not aware of our samskaras in the waking state, they still make themselves felt in the form of fears and obsessions. Primal energy cannot just be dammed up. If it does not find immediate outlet in physical union, it must be appropriately rechannelled or it will give rise to neurosis and other forms of mental illness.

Due to this rechannelling, many aspects of our lives fall under the influence of this energy. The primal energy is diverted to add impetus to some alternative element of our make-up. Freud maintained that it is this diversification of the libido that leads to the development of a richly articulated mental life and creativity.

Freud was not the only psychologist to stress the universal nature of this primal energy. Jung also used the term libido to mean human motivating energy, although he later extended it beyond the sexual. In more recent times Wilhelm Reich, Marcuse and Norman O. Brown have emphasized the significant role of healthy sexuality in all human endeavour.

Psychological theory is therefore in accord with the tantric insight that primal energy informs the full gamut of human emotions and cannot be denied without impairing the natural life processes and depleting our vitality. There is no doubt that our emotions are also a manifestation of this primal energy, which is at once spiritual and sexual. To deny our sexuality then, is to distort a great deal of what most people feel is their essential humanness – their emotional sensitivity. However, in view of our spiritual aims, it is not enough just to give unlicensed expression to this great energy in order to avoid distortion of the personality. We need a method of directing this force to our higher energy centres.

In modern society there is so much guilt, frustration and psychological disease arising from the fact that no one has understood the higher purpose of sexual life in relation to the spiritual awakening. Tantra yoga provides us with both a clear understanding of the nature and purpose of this primal energy and a concrete system of practise for its sublimation.

Tantra is not the narrow path of the ascetic, nor the path of undisciplined indulgence. It is a pathway of heightened experience and intensified awareness, arising from the intelligent understanding and acceptance of our human nature. Tantra is a path to freedom through the establishment of sane, healthy and spiritually oriented means of expressing the life instincts. Tantra does not ask us to renounce the body and its functions, but to renounce the associated conflicts and guilt which stand between us and expanded conscious-ness. What is necessary is that we make appropriate use of

68

our vitality, and that we conduct this primal energy for the purposes of spiritual transformation.

Brahmacharya

Appropriate direction of primal energy for spiritual evolution is called brahmacharya. Brahmacharya is usually translated as celibacy and constitutes one of the elements of sexual sublimation.

Celibacy is total abstinence from sexual interaction. In the shastras celibacy has been defined in eight degrees of strictness – avoidance of: kriya nivritti (conjugal relations), adhvavasaya (desire), sankalpa (thinking about one's beloved), guhyabashana (talking in private), kirtana (praising his/her qualities to others), keli (playing), sparshana (touching), darshana (looking at him/her). When one is observing celibacy for spiritual insight, restraint must extend also to auto-eroticism, and even unconscious expression in dreams.

In India, once a woman is widowed, she is expected to lead a life of strict withdrawal from society in general and male company in particular. Traditionally widows wear only plain white saris, without any jewellery or ornament; they shave their heads; eat only once a day; sleep on a thin mat directly over the hard floor; avoid unnecessary talk in any company. They rise at 4.00 a.m. for puja or sadhana, and spend their days in service of the family and community. Although this tradition is less strictly observed today, it provides us with several hints to help maintain celibacy, whether by force of circumstance or as an act of choice.

Some women choose to refrain from any sexual relationship in order to turn all their time and energies to the pursuit of some creative goal. Others might opt for temporary restraint in order to simplify their emotional life; the better to understand their own emotional dynamics and needs; to investigate talents and potentials previously neglected in favour of the demands of relationship; to develop their resources for sharing love and life with less attachment, greater insight and freedom.

The observance of celibacy for a fixed period of time is called *nastika brahmacharya*. A time is fixed for the duration of this observance – one month, six months, one or several years – according to the advice of the guru. This restraint is generally undertaken for two purposes – to conserve energy for, and thereby facilitate, certain sadhanas; or to provide insight into one's sexual constitution as a basis for both conservation and proper expression of primal energy.

During the period of nastika brahmacharya, one is able to observe even the most subtle manifestations of primal energy in relation to physical desire, social interaction, personal emotional stability and creativity. One becomes much more sensitive to the impact of sexuality in all spheres of life, and one gains greater insight into the consequences of its suppression and expression.

Most important, the sadhaka comes to understand how much vasana (latent desire) she has in this direction. Some women find that much of their primal energy has already been diverted into intellectual or creative pursuits, and that their desire for physical expression is neither very strong nor persistent. For others, regardless of their creative commitments, this drive is much stronger and more enduring. Through the practice of nastika brahmacharya, one is able to understand whether the conjugal relationship is just a habit, or whether it is a powerful force in one's personality. If it is a habit only, then after this sadhana it will just pass away.

Where the demands of primal energy are not so strong, or are already partially sublimated, we could say that such people have 'passive' sexual energy. Where primal energy is less it must be conserved, and where one's sexual constitution is of a passive nature (and this applies to men as much as women) then the observation of celibacy is very helpful in smoothing the path of sadhana.

Observation of celibacy for one's entire lifetime is called *akhanda brahmacharya*, as exemplified in the life of Bheeshma, Mahapita and Hanumanji. Patanjali tells us that through the

70

observation of brahmacharya one gains immense virya –
courage, optimism, endurance – to maintain strength and
optimism for the spiritual adventure.

Grihastha brahmacharya

Hatha yoga can influence the hormones of the body in such
a way that the biological processes of the reproductive system
can be completely stopped. At this same time, the agitation
which is transmitted through the nervous system to the mind
via shukra nadi and vajra nadi can also be blocked, totally.
Yet in yoga the process is not one of suppression, but of
sublimation. Yoga insists on the necessity of sublimation,
and at the same time accepts the necessity of the conjugal
relationship, for the healthy elimination of samskara, as a
tool in the process of evolution.

While some women have a passive sexual constitution, in
others primal energy is more dynamic. Those who have
dynamic sexual energy will never achieve spiritual realization
through premature or enforced celibacy – they must regulate
this energy through experience. Such women (and men), if
they restrain the interactions by force or on impulse, will
always be influenced by their suppressed drives.

That is why, alongside the tradition of renunciation,
there has always been a tradition of progress through
householder life. From vedic times *grihastha ashrama* was
seen as a necessary stage in one's evolution where spiritual
life is stimulated by raising a family and taking an active part
in society. *Consummate* means to complete a marriage through
physical union. It also means to bring to completion (yoga)
or perfection (siddhi), to raise to the highest, or 'crown of',
recalling that Shiva and Shakti are united in sahasrara chakra
at the crown of the head.

Married relations are the expression of the same primal
energy that manifests the universe and moves us towards
spiritual enlightenment. Our spiritual evolution is dependent
on removing the blockages that impede the free flow of this
energy. At certain stages this involves the removal of

inhibitions, complexes and frustrations through a satisfying conjugal relationship. We can grow through pleasure as well as through suffering, and successful married relations bring us greater personal integration. So when we enter grihastha ashrama it is not only a step for the fulfilment of the senses, but for evolution, for the fulfilment of spiritual life.

Celibacy is only part of the definition of brahmacharya, applicable only to some people at some times. The actual definition of this controversial concept does not necessarily involve negation of the conjugal relationship at all. *Brahma* is supreme consciousness, *charya* is movement or behaviour. Brahmacharya is that movement or behaviour that is established in supreme consciousness or leads us to that. Brahmacharya is the behaviour of one whose thoughts, emotions and whole being are directed towards the expansion of consciousness.

Grihastha brahmacharya is the code of sexual conduct laid down for householders in the *Manusmriti, Yagnavalkya Smriti* and similar shastras. Grihastha brahmacharya is not abstention from the conjugal relationship, but the practice of physical union together with certain hatha yoga kriyas for the retention of the orgasm. The immense energy released at this time is conserved by retaining the *bindu*, the bodily fluids secreted at the time of climax. This energy is then directed from mooladhara to the higher energy centres by means of vajroli mudra, sahajoli mudra, uddiyana bandha and moola bandha causing an explosion of samskara and expansion of consciousness.

The concept of retention of *bindu* and prolongation of climax (rajas) is central to the correct understanding of brahmacharya, as indicated in the *Hatha Yoga Pradipika*: "He who controls the bindu and keeps his own rajas separately through vajroli is known as a yogi. His rajas can never be destroyed and in his body the nada merges in the bindu. If in vajroli the bindu and rajas can be kept separately in one's own body, then by the practice of yoga, all kinds of siddhis can be obtained." This also applies to the female experience.

72

Maithuna

According to tantra, the interaction between man and woman may have one of three purposes – procreation, pleasure or samadhi. Householder sadhakas experience this relationship without any inhibitions, conflicts or guilt, as a part of sadhana for samadhi. In general, the climax of this experience is lost before one is able to deepen it, but for spiritual purposes, the climax must be prolonged so that the dormant, 'silent', centres of consciousness are awakened and start to function continuously in daily life.

Maithuna then is not merely physical union, but union with a view to samadhi, the purpose is clear – awakening of sushumna, raising the kundalini from mooladhara chakra and exploding the unconscious areas of the brain.

The practice of maithuna requires strict preparation by both partners. Certain hatha yoga practices must be perfected. Initially a woman develops control of the lower centres through paschimottanasana, shalabhasana, vajrasana, supta vajrasana and siddha yoni asana. Sirshasana is also important in regulating the reproductive hormones and harmonizing influxes to the brain. Moola bandha, uddiyana bandha, shambhavi mudra, sahajoli mudra, and kumbhaka (breath retention) must also become so spontaneous that there is no difficulty in using the techniques at the height of maithuna.

On the emotional level, both husband and wife must be purified of dependency and possessiveness. They must also have transcended the usual stereotyped masculine and feminine behaviour, to the point where both are able to achieve fulfilment by wholehearted acceptance of the role of woman as guru.

It is at the initiative of the woman, and under her guidance, that maithuna takes place. She performs all the necessary preliminaries and marks her husband's forehead, telling him where to meditate. In ordinary relationships the man takes the aggressive role and the woman submits. But in maithuna, the woman takes the lead and the man becomes her medium. A wife must be able to arouse her husband, yet to help him maintain his bindu. If her husband loses control, it is because the woman has not conducted the ritual correctly.

In tantra it is said that Shiva is merely a shava, a corpse, without Shakti. Shakti is the priestess. At the birth of the cosmos Shakti is the creator and Shiva is the witness, so in tantra the woman has the status of the guru and the man of disciple. The tantric tradition is actually passed on from the woman to the man, where it is the woman who initiates.

In the *Hatha Yoga Pradipika* it is said: "That woman who is able to keep her rajas above by means of retention of the orgasm is the real yogini... The practice of vajroli gives siddhi to the body – it becomes handsome, smooth, bright and attractive. This is the divine practice of yoga that gives liberation through enjoyment."

Marriage

In vedic times, marriage and spirituality went hand in hand. In those days, rishis were grihasthas, householders, and the names of Vashishta and Arundati, Atri and Anusuya, Yagynavalkya and Maitreyi have for ages represented both the highest married joy and fidelity, and the highest spiritual attainments. Yet these days wedded bliss seems to be more of a hope than a fact for many women, inner stagnation rather than inner unfoldment.

A mirage

It is a world-wide phenomenon that married women are more vulnerable to mental illness than any other single group of people. Swedish reports indicate that there is a higher probability of mental disorder in married women than single women. American figures reflect an international trend that the more children a married woman has, the more likely she is to suffer psychological distress when compared with her husband, with women who have fewer children, and single women.

The highest incidence of drug use and abuse is not among wayward youth, but housewives. Especially in 'developed' countries, women are turning more and more to tonics and potions that promise them the zest and vitality to pull themselves out of boredom and lethargy. The depressed housewife with her elusive pains and pangs is consuming enormous amounts of medication that does nothing for her basic dissatisfaction. Alarming numbers of women everywhere have become addicted to tranquilizers and antidepressants, and find they simply cannot get through the day without them. These gruesome details, and the growing divorce rates (even in traditional societies), make it seem that a happy marriage is only a mirage.

Means not an end

These sad facts indicate that we have lost sight of the significance of marriage within the context of spiritual development. Both men and women, but women especially, feel that a close relationship is an end in itself, rather than a means to further growth. Women are conditioned to believe that getting married automatically confers security, purpose and everlasting love. They ignore the fact that, married or not, these attainments require unending work on ourselves in the form of an unwavering sankalpa and continuous self-giving. The relationship between a man and a woman can bring tremendous vitality, sparkle and inspiration, provided we understand such a relationship not as a goal achieved, but as a continuous striving towards perfection.

Security

More relationships would succeed if we did not demand from them the impossible. Marriage cannot, for instance, grant us security. Such inner certainty cannot be guaranteed by any external arrangement, nor conferred by someone else. Security is a purely personal achievement. It is harmony and conviction in one's inner essence that results from self knowledge and bestows a poise that remains unaffected by life's ups and downs.

Material security is the most ephemeral. Houses can burn down, possessions can be stolen, currency can become valueless at the stroke of a financier's pen. There is no insurance against war, disease or natural disaster. Nor can we find total emotional security in relationships with others.

No one can love us enough to fill up that emptiness within and possessive love only generates a fear that accentuates this hollowness.

Not security but insecurity is the basic fact of life, and we must recognize it. Instead of chasing after something that does not exist, we must come to terms with the uncertain nature of our existence. Yoga teaches us not to identify with the external, not to try to anchor ourselves in the things we own, nor in other people. The inner loneliness can only be transmuted by the experience of the eternal and unshakable within ourselves, and yoga provides us with the practical means to foster that experience.

Romance and alienation

Marriage is universally associated with love, but most men and women fail to distinguish between love and romance, with the result that many marriages are founded on illusion and flounder on disillusion.

Love sees clearly – it may accept faults but it is not blind to them. On the other hand, romance is a form of enchantment in which one is blind to the real nature of the other person. People are drawn together by a certain feeling of affinity, a greater or lesser correspondence of ideas and feelings, magnified by physical attraction. In the beginning we see only the positive side of each other, emphasizing all that is pleasant in the other's personality. Instead of seeing her potential husband as he really is, a woman 'in love' is more often seeing the projected ideal of her own desire and need. Her need is such that she blinds herself to his faults, and convinces herself that he has qualities that do not exist.

Later this image must crack under the tedium of domesticity and when she begins to see her husband more realistically, the woman is disappointed. As we discover those aspects of the personality that are not in affinity, we tend to exaggerate our husband's faults, or even to feel that he has vices and defects that do not exist. Romance easily changes into resignation or even alienation.

In countries where marriages are arranged, most often even this initial attraction is not present, and women find themselves living with a man who is a virtual stranger. In addition, a woman is under the stress of learning to understand and adjust to his family, whom she is expected to serve with equal love and fidelity.

We can love anybody

In either case, there is no hope and no spiritual gain in succumbing to a permanent revulsion. We must remember that we can learn to love anybody. Everybody has some quality for which he can be respected and loved. Rather than focusing on the disagreeable aspects of someone's personality we must learn to emphasize his virtues. In any garden, we find beauty in many forms. Some flowers have a fascinating shape but no fragrance. Others have a simple appearance, but intoxicate us with their perfume. Some blossom in the sun, some need the protection of shade. Yet we appreciate each one for what it is and do not ask of it to be different. Although we have spontaneous preferences, if we look closely enough at a flower we find some feature that charms.

Yoga encourages us to extend this same acceptance and appreciation to our relationships, and also gives us the practical means to make this a living reality. Obviously, learning to love someone for whom we have developed a dislike is not easy, for it requires a constant alertness and repudiation of the petty and unreasonable in all of us. But we must accept this as a spiritual necessity or continue to suffer frustration and loneliness all our lives. As our sadhana establishes a living link with the divine in ourselves, we open to a real respect for individuality and a genuine joy in the unique miracle of each person in our lives.

Marriage is sadhana

The depression and dissatisfaction of so many married women comes about because they fail to recognize and accept marriage as a sadhana. The transformation of the outer

78

personality and refinement of the inner nature is not an easy process, and we should not expect marriage to be always easy. But once we understand how to use the experiences of marriage and family life for this purpose, then our lives have a new goal and meaning, we find a new strength and joy.

The Mother of Sri Aurobindo Ashram has said: "To unite your physical existences and your material interests, to associate yourselves so as to face together the difficulties and successes, the defeats and victories of life – this is the very basis of marriage – but you know already that it does not suffice. To be one in aspiration and ascension, to advance with the same step on the spiritual path – such is the secret of a durable union."

In India a woman traditionally loves and reveres her husband as her guru, and he loves and reveres her as devi, as a goddess. This does not mean that one or the other is spiritually superior, but that the act of loving is the means to transformation, and that the purpose of marriage is to help one another to become greater than we could be alone.

We have firstly to recognize that difficult situations and the elements we dislike in other people can be our great teachers, for they point out our resistances, prejudices and emotional blockages. What we dislike in others is often some quality that exists unrecognized in ourselves, or which touches a sensitive area of weakness in us. It is our own resistance and attachment that makes certain situations uncomfortable or frustrating, and when we confront such situations repeatedly, we should ask ourselves: "What can I learn from this?" If we are sincere and attentive to our inner voice, that situation will yield up its gift of insight and we will be free of one more limitation.

A husband can learn many things from his wife's way of being and doing, and a woman likewise can make a part of herself those of her husband's strengths and virtues that she might be lacking. With the inspiration and support of a loving relationship we are more willing and able to surrender ourselves to the forces of transformation. It is far easier to be open to someone close whom we respect and love than it is to surrender to an ideal that is distant and abstract. Kahlil Gibran has written:

> *Like sheaves of corn he gathers you unto himself.*
> *He threshes you to make you naked.*
> *He sifts you to free you from your husks.*
> *He grinds you to whiteness.*
> *He kneads you until you are pliant,*
> *And then he assigns you to his sacred fire*
> *that you may become sacred bread for*
> *God's sacred feast.*
> *All these things shall love do unto you that you may know*
> *the secrets of your heart, and in that knowledge become a*
> *fragment in life's heart.*

Karma sannyasa

(by Swami Satyananda Saraswati)

During grihasthashrama you are involved in karma, and these karmas create more karma. They create samskaras to which you are bound because of anasakti or involvement. It is possible to associate with our family, our children, our responsibilities and obligations, either with total attachment or with detachment. However, we have only been taught to base our associations on attachment. Nobody has ever shown us how to love with our own relatives, discharge our duties, solve our problems and interact with our family members, friends, wealth, money and property with detachment. The art of living a detached life is called karma sannyasa.

Detachment is not something that can be developed just by thinking or through any other intellectual process. Unless you have some experience which changes the quality of your mind, you cannot understand what detachment means. In order to understand anasakti, vairagya, sannyasa or detachment, you need more than just an intellectual process. You must have a different quality of mind. And for that purpose, the mind has to be trained and educated.

Intellectually you know that nothing belongs to you and that all is temporary. You may say it every day, but because there is so much mamata, 'mineness' and attachment, whatever happens to someone else affects you too.

You may read the whole of *Yoga Vashishta* but if an accident takes place in your family, you are definitely going to feel it, because the *Yoga Vashishta* has not brought about a fundamental transformation in the structure of your awareness. It has only enlarged the scope of your intellect. At the most you can say, 'Oh, life is temporary', but still you will be struck by the disaster. What is required is a transformation in the realm of awareness, anubhuti or experience, which can be brought about by the practices of dhyana yoga, introspection, mantra and similar techniques.

Most people live the life of a householder, not out of respect or because they think this life has some sort of dignity, but because they are under psychological, emotional or social compulsions. If these compulsions were not there, I don't think we would even like to live this life. That means we do not understand the proper place of grihasthashrama in our evolution. Is the life of a householder meant only for wasting the mind on sensual objects? Is it not a stepping stone to realization? Why was this order created in the Vedas? What was its purpose? Was it progeny? Was it pleasure? Or was it self-realization?

Grihasthashrama is a stepping stone. It is not an end in itself. From grihasthashrama you should step into vanaprasthashram or what I call karma sannyasa. When should you step into vanaprasthashram? At the age of 56, when you have your first heart attack? Or at the age of 76, when you have been completely squeezed of everything? No, the moment you realize that grihasthashrama is the means and not the end, and that within the involvement of life you must develop a deeper and higher, more perpetual, enduring and abiding awareness, immediately get out! Ask your guru for a geru dhoti, a spiritual name, a philosophy to live by and a goal. A karma sannyasin has a goal. A grihastha has no goal, he's just living. Provident fund, property, wealth, educated children – they cannot be the goal or the destiny. A karma sannyasin has one goal, not two, and the destination is one. There cannot be two destinations as far as the total cosmic existence is concerned. Every being, sentient or insentient, mobile or immobile, whether vegetable, mineral, mammal, reptile, human, rakshasa or deva, is just moving towards one destination and that is called perfection. That is called poorna or paramatma tattwa. You may call it God, nirvana, vaikuntha or kaivalya, but it means the same thing. Destination is only one, and when that goal is given to you by your guru, you are a karma sannyasin.

Once a year go alone to any ashram, shave your head, put on geru, sleep on the floor, eat only once a day, practise complete brahmacharya (in thought, word and deed), and live like a poorna sannyasin – no smoking, no transistor radio, no newspaper, no politics, no business, no market, just one thing – your sadhana. Your guru will tell you what to do – japa, likhit japa, read 'Yoga Vashishta' or 'Bhagavad Gita', or practise asana. If he doesn't tell you anything, just work in his kitchen or garden.

Even if you only live the life of a sannyasin for fifteen days, it will enrich you with very deep and abiding experiences, and it will create a new type of mind, personality and man. Then, when you return to grihasthashrama, you will see things with different eyes. There may be births and deaths, marriages, conflicts and quarrels, but you will be able to attend to them as a different person.

When I spoke about karma sannyasa a few years ago, people did not understand it, but now more and more people are beginning to accept this philosophy. You do not have to wear geru to the office; it is not necessary. When you are a karma sannyasin, you must play the role of a perfect householder with the inner attitude of a sannyasin. Karma sannyasa must become the order of the day, and it should revive vanaprastha. Don't wait until you retire. Even while you are married, in grihasthashrama you can be a karma sannyasin.

Other Options

The feminine ideal is moulded in accordance with the division of labour in any society. It has usually fallen to men to engage with the outside world (be it hunting or business) to provide the family with material necessities, and it has been the woman's responsibility to nurture the children and maintain the home in which they are raised. This probably arose because women do need at least some assistance during the final stages of pregnancy and the early life of the baby. This tends to put women in a dependent position on men for at least a few years during their lives. During these years, the horizons of a woman's life are circumscribed almost entirely by the home. Women in such a situation are obliged to become highly conscious of the emotional tone within the family and neighbourhood groups. It is by virtue of her training for the family that a woman is brought up to be passive, compliant and unaggressive, and encouraged to develop the intuition that informs her private world of emotion and sensation.

That women must bear the children is a biological fact. That they must carry the chief burden of tending them is not biological necessity. It is convenient, but convenience is not necessity. There is even less reason for women to maintain the household just because they are females. Among the Todas of southern India the men consider it their sacred duty to do the housework.

To justify the sexual division of the world's work, it was long supposed that women were allotted the household role because of their inability to do much else. It is still widely believed that men have higher intelligence than women and make better use of it. Women are acknowledged as being more intuitive, but in this technological age intuition is devalued and seen as a somewhat dubious compensation for hard-headed rationality. Boys are not taught to follow their intuition but to use their heads, while equal rewards for the same brain work are withheld from girls. Today's world also demands a logical rationale for every action and will not accept intuition as a sufficient basis for decisions, so that women's reasoning is dismissed as chancey and unreliable.

It is widely believed that women are naturally less well endowed with the ability to think, to act, to create. Yet there is no evidence, biological or psychological, for any such incapacity in women. Studies of sex-differences in the achievements of children do not provide any objective support for this bias. Girls and boys have been tested on reading, counting, mathematical reasoning, spatial cognition, abstract reasoning, set-breaking and restructuring, perceptual speed, manual and scientific skills. No significant pattern of difference has emerged. Of the intelligence tests giving a score of total IQ, eleven show no differences between the sexes, three find a difference in favour of women and three in favour of men. Overall, there are no verifiable sex-differences in mental ability to justify the restriction of women to household duties.

If women should be kept at home because they are physically weaker than men, then it should be remembered that few of the higher human achievements require a great deal of muscular strength.

No maternal instinct
It has been argued that there is a natural link between mothers and their offspring, and we have come to speak of a 'maternal instinct' as if it were a basic biological drive that

accounts for the female role in the family. It is almost universally thought that motherhood is the necessary and sufficient condition for female fulfilment; that motherhood is enough to provide ultimate satisfaction for every woman and the only way in which complete wholeness can be enjoyed.

Next to the instinct for self-preservation, the sex drive is the strongest of man's biological impulses and the outcome of this is usually reproduction. But the impulse to maternity is not in itself a biological motivating force and therefore is not common to all female humans. The 'maternal instinct' is the result of generations of social training combined with a need to take the most rewarding and enriching view of an (hitherto) unavoidable situation. Males are born with all the physical equipment necessary for them to become fathers, but we do not speak of a 'paternal instinct'.

No man would accept the dictum that he was born first and foremost to be a father or that fatherhood is the only role that will bring him personal fulfilment. Men have always gained their rewards from a wide range of activities, and fatherhood often plays only a small part in a man's life or no part at all. Yet we do not say that men who do not have children are 'unnatural', which is how we describe women who don't want to have children. It is also widely tolerated that a child's biological father may take no part in his upbringing. Yet a woman who leaves her child to be raised by another is considered evil or crazy or, at best, an unfortunate victim of fate.

When looking at the unhappiness of women who want to bear children but are physically unable to do so, many people would argue that this is evidence for the existence of a maternity instinct which, unfulfilled, can lead only to frustration. Firstly, not all sterile women are unhappy. Secondly, these women did not choose to be childless and much of their unhappiness comes from the feeling that they are being deprived of something. Moreover, in a world where maternity is seen as the sole reason and purpose behind feminine existence, childless women are perceived as somehow incomplete and are subjected to a lot of misplaced sympathy and pity which does not ease their situation. Those women who have successfully reconciled their disappointment have turned to other occupations, and a good many know the joys of motherhood through adopting children.

Anthropological evidence does not support the notion that the sense of fulfilment which comes from tending children is based on the satisfaction of an instinctive drive. There are studies in which hardly a trace of maternal instinct appears. In one New Guinea tribe which Dr Mead studied, the women looked on a maternal role with unconcealed repugnance; the rare woman who was 'motherly' towards her children was treated with scorn. More striking yet are the Mbaya studied by Claude Levi-Strauss. They look with such disfavour on motherhood that a partial substitute is used for reproduction. Mbaya warriors capture youngsters from other tribes and adopt them, raising them as their own.

More telling than these isolated examples, however, is a universal fact: few human societies have considered the link between mothers and their offspring so natural, so fulfilling, that they have neglected to teach women that motherhood is their duty and their destiny. Indeed, the more civilized a society becomes the more insistent this training is likely to become; for the richer the human world grows in its range of activities, the wider is the choice of life-possibilities outside motherhood and the family.

The choice

It is ridiculous to say that women will no longer want to marry or have children. The householder way of life is that path most people prefer as best suited to their needs and desires, and the rewards of living with and caring for children are great indeed. After all, many people choose to make it their life's work to nurse or teach children because they find this so stimulating and enriching. (Since many of these people are men there is no question of this being the outcome of a rechannelled maternal instinct.)

The widespread availability of contraception is offering a freedom of choice regarding motherhood. Women are now in a position to choose motherhood and family life rather than have it thrust on them unthinkingly. Some women will feel that motherhood is not for them, or not at this time. On the other hand, a woman who actively chooses the mother's role will find it more rewarding than one who accepts reluctantly. She will be more positive, competent and loving. She will be more creative in finding patterns of relating that are enriching to herself and her family.

Nevertheless, a re-evaluation of the inevitability of motherhood and family life will lead women to examine the present criteria for the 'woman's work' that causes distress to so many. They will be freed from guilt at not being always content to stay at home and mind the children. There is an option here that should be investigated in the light of a woman's individual needs for integration. Recognition of the fact that there is a choice is also a step to revaluing the work and lifestyles of those women who do not marry.

Single women

There have always been women who have actively and positively chosen an alternative to marriage. Yoginis, the priestesses of ancient Greece and Phoenicia, witches, nuns, saints and religious aspirants throughout time – all these women have found fulfilment outside marriage and mother-hood. In families everywhere there have always been unmarried women who are useful and loved as daughters, sisters and aunts, rather than as wives and mothers.

Today more and more women are looking beyond the traditional feminine roles for the full expression of their potential. Just as once there were mighty queens and empresses, now women are once again taking part in the government of their countries, even at the highest levels. Women have entered the law courts and surgeries; they are engineers and architects; scientists, teachers, nurses and artists; psychologists, social workers and executives. Women are increasingly taking and making opportunities to lead constructive and fulfilling lives in a world that was once the sole prerogative of men.

Prejudice

Despite this apparent emancipation of women, there still remains more or less subtle discrimination against them. The fact is that women in the professions and high levels of commerce are a very small minority. The majority hold relatively low positions in business and industry or are engaged as domestic servants. Most women are employed as waitresses, clerks, typists, secretaries and production-line factory hands. Of course this is partly the result of women treating their jobs as a stop-gap to marriage or as a means of supplementing a low family income. However, equal opportunity of employment is still to come.

Many employers feel that women are somehow less competent and they prefer to hire men. Unfortunately, in most cases, a woman must have higher qualifications than a man in order to hold the same job. It is also true that the majority of men (because of their conditioning) feel insulted if they must work under a female superior, and this problem of personnel management is often the cause of executives failing to promote qualified women. Most people expect that every woman will eventually marry and have children so that training women for higher positions is regarded as a waste of time and money. It is extremely difficult for single women to convince people that they take their work seriously and they have no desire to abandon it for marriage.

In addition to job prejudice, single women have also to face legal discrimination. In most countries it has slowly (and often only recently) come about that women may hold property in their own right rather than have it administered in trust by some male member of the community. However, single women have great trouble securing a lease to rent a house or flat, let alone trying to raise the finance to buy a home. Single women are considered bad credit risks simply because they are not married and therefore do not have the dubious guarantee of a husband's income.

Society still feels that women should marry and a lot of pressure to do so is exerted by family and friends. A woman who does not marry is not only alienating her family, she is felt to be risking poverty, moral danger and, above all, a lonely old age. The fact that marriage is no safeguard against these misfortunes does not enter the argument. This situation is much worse for a girl who would like to marry, but for some reason has not or cannot. She is divided because she has not actively chosen the single state, and she is more vulnerable to that self-doubt which arises under constant criticism from others.

The general lack of social acceptance of unmarried women is betrayed in the pity (or mockery) of words like 'old maid'. While the description 'bachelor' indicates only that a man is unmarried, the feminine equivalent, 'spinster', conjures up an image of a brittle, waspish woman whose failure to marry has dried up her vitality and humanity. More recently has come the trendy description 'bachelor girl', with its unsavoury overtones of loose living and self-indulgence. On the other hand, a 'career woman' is perceived as cold and ruthless, a heartless automaton whose concern with her work earns not respect but distaste. It is not considered that single women might withdraw themselves, or become critical and angry, simply because they are always besieged by social hostility to their way of life.

A single woman has to be impeccable, for if she has any fault it is blamed on her single state. If people find they dislike her personality, they assure themselves that 'all she needs is a man'. No matter how happy or successful a woman is, she is always taunted by the fact that 'she couldn't get herself married'. It seems to be beyond most people to accept that some women genuinely do not wish to marry. Women are opting out of marriage in increasing numbers, but in doing so they are joining an unacknowledged battle for social acceptance.

More time for yoga

Single women find in yoga a relief from their tensions and an enhancement of their way of life. The practice of yoga promotes detachment and gives a woman the inner poise to rise above petty criticism with serenity. By encouraging the attitude of perfect work with perfect detachment, yoga transforms a woman's career into a means of attaining higher awareness. No matter what kind of work she is doing, this attitude brings the realization that her work is not just a means of earning a living, but is also a powerful spiritual practice. With fewer responsibilities and demands on her time, the single woman has more time to devote to self-culture through yoga, and she will gain from yoga the strength, confidence and personal magnetism that will speak for themselves in justification of her lifestyle.

Sannyasa

We do not have to change our social status in order to grow spiritually. If we are married it is not necessary to dissolve the relationship or change our way of life. Sadhana in married life can definitely take us to the heights.

On the other hand there are women who, by choice, will never marry. Their personalities are oriented to a different style of life. To such women seeking the highest spiritual attainments, for those women who want simply to be useful, yoga offers the sannyasa way of life, leading to spontaneity, harmony and wisdom.

In renouncing other ways of life, a woman does not lose anything. If she has maternal feelings, these are given more universal expression and hundreds of children, old and young, will benefit from her love. Instead of serving husband and children in the home, she will widen her sphere to serve the whole of humanity. A sannyasin renounces the super-ficialities of the world only so that the world can be known and experienced more fully. Sannyasa is a creative lifestyle that progressively eliminates all mental complexes and disturbances. There is simply no scope in this active and

90

stimulating life for neurosis or depression. Sannyasa transforms the mind into a perfect instrument that transmits not confusion but wisdom, not unhappiness but bliss.

Once she has become a sannyasin, a woman is outside sexual distinctions and is freed from pressure to adhere to any particular role just because of her biology. A sannyasin has no role, she is free to adopt any course of action that enables her to be of service. Through sannyasa a woman can most fully help herself by helping others. In opting for sannyasa she is pledging herself to a thorough-going involvement with life that cannot fail to take her to her spiritual goal. Sannyasa is the ultimate in women's liberation.

Women and sannyasa
(by Swami Satyananda Saraswati)
In the history of yoga, women have always been in the majority. Count the number here in this assembly; go to any yoga class, satsang or ashram and you will find more women than men. The fact that you will always find more women involved in spiritual movements is not due to a recent development, it is because there has been a recent revival.

Throughout the last few centuries, women have been kept suppressed and denied the fundamental rights of equality. They were also barred from spiritual life. Perhaps the reason for this was that we wanted to exploit them for our carnal objectives. I am sure my suspicion is correct. If women were allowed to practise spiritual life and encouraged to raise their awareness, then how could they be used as victims of our carnality?

Look at the status of women. Until recently they were only encouraged to be wives and mothers and nothing more. They were conditioned in such a way that they did not know how to deny, refuse or resist. It is only now that women are beginning to break free of the old tradition. However, in the western countries they have always been completely excommunicated from the spiritual cloister. Whenever I have visited monasteries in the west, all the female sannyasins

91

who were accompanying me were not allowed beyond the cloisters. It is completely different in the tradition of yoga where men and women can live and interact with each other.

Since the beginning of yogic history, women have always played a major role and many of them have even been gurus and saints. Shiva is believed to be the first guru and the founder of tantra and yoga. Do you know who his first disciple was? Parvati, his counterpart, wife or shakti. If you read the tantric texts you will find they commence with 'Parvati asked'. Therefore, the knowledge of tantra and yoga was first imparted to a woman. And in the yogic culture, when reference is made to a relationship, the woman is always mentioned first. We say 'Sita Ram' not 'Ram Sita', 'Radha Krishna' not 'Krishna Radha' and 'Gauri Shankara' not 'Shankara Gauri'.

In the Tibetan and Hindu traditions of tantra there are eighty-four siddhas and out of these, sixty-four were yoginis. and in Kashmir there was a great lady saint named Lalla. She was always completely naked. Often her devotees would ask, 'Lalla, why don't you put on clothes?' and she used to taunt them, 'Do you see my body or do you see my soul?'

In the Upanishads you will find many references to great women saints and philosophical debates between the male and female yogis. One notable reference is to a very clever lady called Garghi, a renowned scholar and great sannyasini.

When Shankaracharya wrote his famous text on tantra, *Ananda Lahari*, he commenced it with a very touching verse – "without Shakti, how can Shiva create anything?" Shiva is only the silent witness, Shakti is the creator. That is why, in the tantric tradition, the woman is the initiator.

There are two traditions existing in the world. One is matriarchal and the other is patriarchal. Judaism, Christianity and Islam are patriarchal, whereas Hinduism, Buddhism, Zoroastrianism, Shintoism, Taoism and Confucianism are all matriarchal. The matriarchal religions are very accommodating religions. They have a great deal of understanding and compassion for others which reflects the feminine nature.

Matriarchal religions have been responsible for the beautiful things in life, such as the fine arts, yoga, tantra, dance, music, painting and so on. Patriarchal religions are non-compromising and they have produced powerful warriors and developed strong administrations. They have also prevented the women from coming forward.

However, in the last one and a half centuries, the women in the west have been becoming more open, and changes are also slowly taking place in the east. As I told you in the beginning, there has also been a recent revival in the tradition of female sannyasins and for this, I am responsible. In the early sixties and seventies, when I began to initiate women into sannyasa, there was a great commotion amongst the orthodox people. But as the years rolled by, they had no other option than to follow my trail. Now they have more female disciples than I have.

My personal philosophy is: women are very sincere and obedient. They are honest and hard working, and when they work with you, they keep you relaxed all the time. I would also say that one of the most important reasons for the success of my work is the induction of females into the movement. I do not mean that men are useless; they have their own place, but in the scheme of creation, I believe women are superior.

Woman is one of the finest creations of the creator and there is no reason why she should be barred from spiritual life. Women are very psychic by nature and we should allow them to raise their consciousness and develop this part of their personality. Why should they not become clairvoyants, telepaths, prophets, scholars and sannyasins?

The Goddess Within

Astarte, the Great Mother, dearly loved her son Tammuz, the Green One, the vegetation that clothes the earth. Fascinated by his beauty and desiring him for her own, the Queen of the Underworld one day kidnapped Tammuz and took him to her domain. Astarte wailed and lamented. Her face shrivelled and the flesh dropped from her bones. Inconsolable, she bound up her hair and took to wandering the whole world in search of her son, but he was nowhere in this world to be found.

After some time, the sun took pity on Astarte and revealed the secret of her son's whereabouts. The Great Goddess was sorely grieved, but not overcome. In her wrath she brought down a mighty curse on the whole earth: "Let all mankind perish! Let there be no rain, no warmth, no crops if my son be not returned to me". Because she was such a powerful goddess her wishes were commands and all the wide earth became cold and barren.

While the earth shivered, Astarte set out on her arduous journey. She knocked loud and insistent below the foreboding portal at the entrance to the Underworld where the leering gatekeeper demanded her crown as price of passage. She gave it. Through darkness and evil air, past weird and grotesque presences she made her rough and torturous descent to the centre of the Underworld. As she traversed the six remaining gates that stood between her and her goal, each gatekeeper demanded a token which she gave and did not heed the cost. Emerging through the last gate she stood naked where she confronted the Queen of the Underworld and bargained for the life of her son. Above and below the whole earth was hushed as the forces of light and dark, life and death, engaged in their contest of strength.

Finally Astarte prevailed and her son was restored to her. Tammuz was reborn into the world of light, bringing joy to the world in the celebration of spring.

Myth...

In the twilight language of myth we convey understandings we know intuitively to be true, giving expression to experience too deep for logical comprehension. The Astarte myth can awaken many interpretations, but on one reading this is the story of every spiritual seeker. Astarte's desire to be reunited with Tammuz is the deep impulse in all of us to merge again in supreme consciousness. Her journey into the Underworld is the exploration of the depths of our being which we must all undertake to reach our goal. The struggle between the forces of light and darkness is the contest that takes place in every soul. The Queen of the Underworld is the powerful ego which would chain us in ignorance forever. The seven gatekeepers are the trials and obstructions of daily life which, met with the right attitude, help us to throw off attachments and negativity. The seven gates are the seven chakras, and the re-emergence of Astarte and Tammuz into the world of light is our own rebirth into higher consciousness.

Myths arise from the collective unconscious, which is the storehouse of the whole experience of the race concerning the true nature of women. This level of our being welds together the complements and the contradictions that defy intellectual explanation, forging the symbols that influence us from beyond the realm of waking consciousness. Myths galvanize people and serve as guidelines for personal growth. Thus the Astarte myth has relevance for all women. Although the 'woman of women', Astarte exemplifies courage, determination and personal power. She mourns the loss of her son but does not allow grief to overwhelm her. She does not just sit passively and suffer, but does all she can to remedy the situation. Although loving, she is not weakened by her love. Astarte is undaunted by the rigours of her journey, and throughout displays the courage and determination we all need to see ourselves clearly. The great Goddess is the supernatural embodiment of the creative forces of the universe, inspiring mankind to worship from the very beginnings of the race.

...and symbol

Over recent decades archaeologists have gathered an enormous accumulation of evidence indicating that Mother Goddess worship played an important part in the lives of our Stone Age ancestors – as it still does in India, Africa and some other parts of the world. This is reflected not only in cave paintings, but also in the numerous statues and figurines of women carved in stone, bone, antler and even mammoth tusk. Some of these date back 25,000 years, and such figures outnumber similar carvings of men by about ten to one. Although most of the figurines depict naked women, they are not usually considered erotic, or art for art's sake. For many reasons anthropologists have concluded that they were part of a magical or religious tradition. Most are highly stylized or symbolic, giving special emphasis to the breasts, buttocks and genitals, suggesting that the Goddess was regarded as the infinitely fertile, the supreme creator.

Not only is this tradition as old as the race itself, it appears to have been almost universally practised. Goddess figures have been found in Spain, France, Germany, Austria, Czechoslovakia and Russia. They also appear in the Near East in Turkey, all along the Tigris and Euphrates rivers, in Egypt, and, of course, in India. On the other side of the world among the Australian aborigines whose cultural inheritance is almost unchanged from the Stone Age, the deity of the Dreamtime was female. Along with a few other primitive peoples, they did not understand biological paternity or accept the necessary connection between sexual intercourse and conception. The female was revered as the giver of life, and the role of the male was not connected with the conceiving of life. Hence, woman was all-powerful; it was she and only she, who had the gift to bring new life into the world. Even throughout the area now known as the Bible Lands, the land of the Hebrews, the most common ritual objects from the Late Bronze Age (c.1500–1300 BC) are plaques depicting the Goddess Astarte. The same or similar objects recur right into biblical times.

Worshipped in many lands, the Goddess was also known by many names – Isis in Egypt, Nana in Sumeria, Ishtar in Babylon, Ashtoreth or Astarte in Assyria, Aphrodite in Greece, Venus in Rome. In China she is the Teh that manifests the Tao and in the tantric tradition of India she is Shakti or Devi. No matter what name they used, the peoples of all these regions worshipped the supreme as Goddess Mother.

We must not make the mistake of associating the worship of the Great Goddess only with mankind's primitive infancy. The stronghold of the Goddess was among the communities around the Mediterranean basin, in the Near and Middle East, and in India, in fact, the whole of the area that has come to be recognized as 'the cradle of civilization'. It was in this region that mankind moved from simple hunting and gathering to animal husbandry and agriculture, and it was here that writing was developed – all under the auspices of the Great Goddess.

Sumeria was the predecessor of Babylon as the great city culture of this region, and we have evidence dated around 3000 BC that the Goddess was worshipped in a temple served almost exclusively by priestesses. Now the temple was the key institution of early civilization. It appears to have owned the land, the herds of animals and most material property. The Sumerians credited the invention of clay tablets and the art of writing to the Goddess and the earliest known examples of writing were found in the temple of the Queen of Heaven at Erech in Sumeria. The Minoan civilization on Crete was one of the most advanced in prehistory, materially (they even had indoor bathrooms and flush toilets) and culturally (influencing the development of the later Greek culture). Yet the Minoans worshipped the Goddess as a wasp-waisted, bare-breasted lady adorned with snakes. No one would dispute the pre-eminence of the Egyptian civilization, where it was believed that the Goddess existed when nothing else had been created. Indeed, it was she who enthroned in the sky Ra, the Sun God, the deity of the Pharaohs. Civilization began, and flourished, among those societies which revered the Great Goddess as supreme creator.

The myths and ritual surrounding the Goddess arise from the collective unconscious and reflect the intuitive understanding of the whole human race with regard to the origin of creation and the forces acting in the cosmos. Some conscious insight into these intuitions can be obtained from the scriptures and the ritual emblems that have survived from the past. There is endless written evidence coming down to us from the stone and clay tablets of the various ancient societies of Egypt, the Middle East, and from as far away as China and Africa. These attest to the awesome power of the Goddess, who was regarded as the suprahuman embodiment of the creative energy of the universe.

A tablet from Thebes in Egypt (about 1400 BC) announces: "In the beginning there was Isis; Oldest of the Old. She was the Goddess from whom All Being arose. She was the Great Lady Mistress of the two Lands of Egypt, Mistress of Shelter, Mistress of Heaven, Mistress of the House of Life, Mistress of the Divine Word. She was the Unique. In all Her great and wonderful works She was a wiser magician and more excellent than any other deity."

To the Babylonians (1800–700 BC) Ishtar was the "One who walked in terrible Chaos, and brought life by the Law of Love, and out of Chaos brought us harmony."

The following litany from *Durgashatanamastotram* recited in India is typical of the epithets applied to the Goddess wherever she was worshipped: "Pure one; essence of all; knowledge; action; the Supreme one; giver of higher wisdom; who art all; whose love is unbounded; existence; holder of many weapons; virgin; maiden; youthful; ascetic one; old Mother; giver of strength."

The visual symbols of the Goddess are just as eloquent in testimony of her many-sided creative power. One golden medallion found in the Near East is embossed with a beautiful woman holding a lotus, symbol of the cosmic life force among Phoenicians, Egyptians and Indians. It is similar to many Bronze Age plaques depicting Astarte as a naked woman holding a lily stalk, or in some cases, a serpent. The famous statue *Venus of Willendorf* has the enormous pregnant belly and swollen breasts typical of many of the 'Venus figurines' found throughout Europe and suggestive of creative fecundity. Diana of Ephesus, the heathen Goddess denounced by Saint Paul in his Epistles to the Ephesians, is represented as a voluptuous woman with a thousand breasts, symbol of loving nurture and abundance. These are all manifestations of the Great Goddess in her Earth Mother aspect; she brings to birth and nourishes what is born. All the Vegetarian Mothers, like Demeter and Isis, share this kind of energy. The image is a joyful spiral like the conch shell, the cornucopia (Horn of Plenty).

Force for evolution
The cosmos is neither simple nor immutable, every reflection being a refraction that eventually reveals another face. Nor are the intuitions embodied by the Great Goddess so simplistic as to fashion only those deities that fit into this 'good fairy' mould. In recognition of the destructive power of the universe, the capacity for dissolution and re-absorption, mankind also pays homage to the Goddess as universal death-dealer. In this aspect she is portrayed as terrifying and gruesome, usually with the tongue stiff and poking out. Medusa was such a one, turning men into stone if they dared look directly into her eyes, the awful concentration of her

power being symbolized by her snaky coiffure. She brings to mind the Mexican Coatlicue who is all dressed up to kill in a skirt of writhing serpents. Other Death Mothers are Lilith and Hecate who have come to personify the evil witch who dabbles in black, rather than white, magic.

Yet neither nature nor supernature is categorically black or white, and there are other dimensions of power personified in various Goddesses. One Middle Eastern stone relief displays a woman with four arms sitting astride a tiger, symbolizing her command over the violent passions of our lower nature. This imagery is very close to the portraits of Indian Durga, who also has four arms, blood-coloured garments and rides bareback on a lion.

Evidence of this kind suggests that the Goddess was not only content to create, but also acted as a force for spiritual evolution. This is corroborated by the rites of other deities such as Artemis, Diotima and Sophia who were patrons and embodiments of wisdom. In Greece, the Muse was invoked by all musicians, dancers and poets. In India she is Saraswati, mistress of all the fine arts, of learning and of knowledge, both temporal and spiritual. Such Goddesses are often associated with open fields and the out-of-doors, suggesting that they are not domesticated like the Earth Mothers who tend the ovens and home fires. They represent the forces that intensify mental and spiritual life until it reaches a point of ecstasy and they are often depicted dancing. All Virgin Mothers (including Mary, Mother of Jesus) embody this power: 'virgin' meaning 'unconditioned, free' signifying that their function is not to bring children into the world but to bring mankind to a state of ecstasy.

The might of the Goddess defies simplification and it is not surprising to find that the most powerful manifestations transcend all distinctions. The tantric Kali is a prime example, simultaneously wielding the forces of creation, destruction and evolution. Kali Ma, Mother Kali, the deity worshipped by Sri Ramakrishna, is a voluptuous woman as black as night, ornamented with a necklace of skulls and girdle of severed hands. Of her two left arms, the upper one is raised to strike, sword in hand, while from the other dangles the severed head of a demon. Of her two right hands, one is raised in *vara mudra*, the gesture of bestowing blessings, and the other displays *abhaya mudra* to dispel fear. She laughs wildly, tongue lolling drunkenly from a bloody mouth, as she dances in abandon on the corpse of Time.

Kali is at one and the same time creator, preserver and destroyer of the universe. She is infinite bliss trampling time underfoot in the dance of eternal creation. She ruthlessly destroys the demons of our lower natures while protecting her devotees from the depredations of spiritual ignorance. She sustains and protects all who come to her, fulfilling their desires and bestowing the ultimate blessing of divine ecstasy and liberation. Kali encompasses all the disparate aspects of the Great Goddess – granting life, releasing us into death and dancing us into ecstasy beyond both: the focus of all the dimensions of power that constitute the cosmos.

In tantra this cosmic power is called Shakti (from the root meaning 'to be able') and is given different forms and names according to the specific function and sphere of operation. Shakti is the creative impulse that manifests the universe in response to inspired consciousness. Creation is the play of energy before consciousness, the dance of Shakti before Shiva. In a universe that is increasingly recognized by science as a matrix of interlocking energy fields, Shakti is all.

In the *Mahanirvana Tantra* Shiva addresses Shakti: "You are the supreme manifestation of Brahman, the supreme consciousness, and from you has come the entire universe. You are its mother. You are the origin of all manifestations. You are the form of everything. Your root is in Brahman who is actionless. It is you, moved by his desire, who creates, protects and withdraws this world with all that moves and is motionless. Therefore, by worshipping you your devotees will surely reach the supreme."

Shakti has a dual nature. It is Shakti as *Maya* who enveils us in this world of sensual experience and delusion. Yet it is the direct personal perception of the Shakti *Kundalini* that leads us to enlightenment. Tantra recognizes that the supreme is one, beyond polarity, but that it manifests as Shiva (male), consciousness, and Shakti (female), energy. However, tantra emphasizes the rituals of the Goddess Shakti, for these constitute the practical means (yoga sadhana) for the arousal and unification of the energies that are necessary to propel us to the peaks of expanded consciousness.

Renaissance

Mother Goddess worship is still a vital tradition in India where Shakti is revered in her most popular form as Kali. However, the decline of Goddess worship throughout the rest of the world does not invalidate the realizations and practices encoded in these rituals. It reflects a shift in the balance of power amongst mankind, rather than a restructuring of the forces of the universe. The change appears to have started around 3000 BC and to have been connected with the invasions of new peoples from the north. Successive waves of invasions lasted at least a thousand, perhaps three thousand years.

The new peoples are variously known as Indo-Europeans, Indo-Iranians or, simply, Aryans. Their origins are uncertain, but they probably descended from the Stone Age communities of far northern Europe. Whereas the devotees of the Goddess were generally settled agricultural communities, the Aryans were herdsmen who worshipped a male Sky-God. This deity sent down rain for their pastures in return for animal (sometimes human) sacrifice. These societies were patriarchal and made a profession of fighting, for which they are known as 'battle axe cultures'. Wherever they invaded they conquered and ruled, bringing with them their male gods of storm and fire (Indra and Agni).

The Aryans reached Punjab in far western India where they encountered the indigenous Dravidians, who had an advanced culture similar to that of the Chaldeans. The Dravidians had abandoned blood sacrifice and meat-eating, paying peaceful homage to the forces of nature represented by the *lingam* and the Goddesses Kali and Durga. The Dravidian culture was essentially a tantric culture. The Aryans brought with them the elements of what was to develop into the Hindu culture – Sanskrit, the caste system and new male gods led by Indra. However, perhaps because they worshipped several deities rather than just one, they were more tolerant of the Dravidian deities and worship of the Goddess continues, although its bastions were (and are) in Bihar, Orissa and Assam – the points furthest from the centre of Aryan influence. Consequently, the potent mysteries which were lost to the Eleusinians and western culture were preserved, complete and uncorrupted, by the tantrics of India who have zealously passed their knowledge from guru to disciple for thousands of years. Since about 500 AD this oral tradition has been supplemented by written scriptures and today the two combined are a major vehicle for the tantra yoga renaissance that is now taking place.

An inspiration

After hundreds of years of dormancy, the Great Mother is again awake in the human psyche. The Goddess symbol is one with impact for modern women, reforming the forgotten primal energy that integrates and activates a woman's deepest potentials. Today's woman must be able to destroy any obsolete or irrelevant concepts that hobble her development. While nurturing her own inner light she does not neglect others, and she is careful to preserve all that is good in her present way of life. Such a woman is open to new perceptions that enable her to create new and more joyful ways of being. Activating her dormant powers, every woman can dance in eternal bliss on the corpse of her lesser self.

Special Applications

Backache

Backache claims over two million new sufferers every year in the USA. World-wide, doctors estimate that more than thirty percent of us will suffer from backache some time or another, making this disturbance almost as common as the common cold. Major organic diseases of the bones of the spine such as tuberculosis, cancer and osteomyelitis are rare causes of spinal pain. Even slipped discs, fractures and dislocations account for only a very small proportion of backache cases. There are many other common causes of pain in the spine which can definitely be successfully managed by yoga techniques.

Different pains

What we loosely call backache is a vague hold-all for a variety of different problems, each requiring individual understanding and attention.

Prolapsed disc commonly called 'slipped disc' is the rupturing of one of the fibrous pads found between the spinal bones. The jelly-like fluid within the disc spills out and towards the spine, pressing against one of the spinal nerves. Pain may be felt in the waist or lower back, and there may be shooting pain or tingling-numbness in the legs. The pain increases during deep breathing.

Sciatica is a sharp, shooting pain in the buttocks or back of the leg due to pressure of a slipped disc against the sciatic

107

nerve. This pain may be almost continuous, but is most severe while standing, walking or lifting.

Spondylitis is vertebral inflammation which causes pressure on the nerves emerging from the spinal cord. In some cases the vertebra slips at the base, or bony outgrowths may develop, in both cases exerting further pressure on the nerves. Cervical spondylitis is characterized by pain in the neck and shoulders, sometimes extending down either arm. Pain in the upper back increases with deep breathing, and there can be pain while turning. Lumbar spondylitis affects the lower back. Ankylosing spondylitis is accompanied by growth between the vertebrae which ultimately fuses all the bones together, depriving the spine of its flexibility. This rigidity is sometimes called bamboo spine or poker spine.

Low back pain

By far the most common kind of backache is low back pain which is not related to any specific organic problem such as slipped disc, arthritis, tumour, or tuberculosis. Recent studies have shown that these causes, together with pain after fracture or dislocation, account for only twenty percent of cases. Four out of five backaches are due simply to weak back muscles, and inflexibility of muscles and tendons – both of which can fortunately be rectified by an appropriate yoga program.

Causes

The most common cause of low back pain is poor posture. We do not sit, stand, sleep or bend efficiently and correctly because of weakened muscles, lack of exercise and sedentary life. Poor posture can itself give rise to pain, and is exaggerated by fallen arches in the foot or similar problems, and by wearing high-heeled shoes. Postural defects also render the muscles more susceptible to sprain from sudden jerks or strain while lifting, bending or driving.

Referred pain in the back has its cause not in the back or spine, but in the abdominal or reproductive organs.

108

Constipation and gas pain cause a dull backache, or exaggerate existing pain. In women, retroverted or prolapsed uterus usually causes back pain.

Congestion of the pelvis due to intestinal or other infections is another possible source of back pain. In women, vaginal infection or even bladder infections can be associated with backache. The congestion of the reproductive system associated with certain hormonal imbalances is at the root of much of the dull backache experienced by women prior to menstruation. This can be relieved by easing the congestion through asanas, and ultimately overcome by restoring hormonal harmony.

Abdominal weakness is another major contributing factor in backache. This is especially true in women, who generally have weaker abdominal muscles by constitution, and in whom muscle tone is often lost after pregnancy.

There are no bones over the abdomen, and all the abdominal organs are supported and kept in place by various muscles that are anchored to the spine. The lumbar spine and pelvis provide a solid support from behind and the abdominal muscles provide a firm but elastic support from the front. If the abdominal muscles become weak and flabby, the inner organs fall forward, causing a pull on the vertebrae behind. Where the abdomen is also heavy and distended due to overweight or digestive problems, there is also a demand on the back muscles for compensation. Moreover, when abdominal muscles are weak, our posture is altered, putting further strain on the back. Particularly for women most cases of backache will be relieved by strengthening the abdominal muscles, and very often this is all that is required.

Emotional factors

Constant or excessive emotional tension is always reflected somewhere in the body, and if the back is your weakest point, then emotional tensions will lead to chronic muscle tension and low backache. In common parlance, the coccyx is referred to as the 'tail bone', indicating that these are not only the last bones, but also those that would be the support of our tail if we had one. If man once had a tail, then the coccyx is the vestige, the last remnant of that tail. In lower animals, the tail is used for keeping away insects, for balance, and to express emotions like anger and fright. On the whole, mankind has dispensed with the necessity of a tail by evolving better ways to express his feelings. Yet in all cultures, there are many crude but expressive gestures and sayings which reflect an instinctive, if unconscious, connection between negative emotions and this part of the body.

When we are subject to frustration, discontent, sexual and emotional tensions, this ancient link is reactivated, and the tension is translated into stiff and painful back muscles.

Acute and chronic pain

Acute backache is a severe and sudden pain which intensifies with every movement, or prohibits movement altogether. Acute backache requires immediate bed rest. A hard mattress and lying on the stomach (makarasana, advasana) are recommended. Further relaxation through massage, hot and cold compresses, and the practice of yoga nidra will also reduce the pain. Once acute pain has subsided, it is best to seek competent professional advice, and then to start on a simple yoga program.

Slipped disc is usually felt first as an acute and immobilizing pain, sharp and well localized at first, then constant as inflammation increases. Where the ruptured fluid presses on the sciatic nerve, acute sciatica will prevent standing or walking. Sciatica may become milder but chronic, with pain reappearing every morning on rising.

Chronic backache is less intense but of longer duration, becoming a daily discomfort for years together. Most forms of low back pain fall in this category, punctuated by bouts of acute pain under physical or emotional duress.

In both cases a thorough medical investigation should be undertaken, and yoga practices commenced only under the supervision of an experienced yoga therapist.

110

Yoga therapy

Yoga helps overcome backache by providing the systematic exercise that strengthens the back and the means to discharge tension before it manifests as physical pain.

Asanas: The mainstay of yoga therapy in these cases, strengthening and relaxing the muscles on either side of the spine, and maintaining the health of spinal discs and supporting ligaments. Encroaching spinal stiffness can be reversed by proper asana practice, and the spine restored to correct alignment. This relieves pressure on the nerves that emerge from between the vertebrae, promoting flexibility for the full range of spinal movements. Asanas also make a major contribution by tightening and strengthening flabby abdominal muscles so that they can play their correct role in maintaining proper posture and pelvic support.

Where digestive problems aggravate back pain, laghoo shankhaprakshalana is a great help. It relieves constipation and gas problems, tones the intestines and reduces congestion. The twisting and bending postures used in this practice are also beneficial for backache in their own right.

Backward bending asanas bring considerable relief in all kinds of back pain, and also form part of any program for restoring hormonal balance and relieving congestion of the reproductive system. Women will find that both kinds of difficulty will disappear with the one yoga program, provided it is properly designed and practised regularly.

Yoga nidra: While asanas are efficient at relieving back pain, steps must also be taken to avoid the build up of emotional tensions that can precipitate such pain. Some form of yogic relaxation and meditation is therefore an essential element of every sadhana routine. In cases of backache, meditation techniques that require a sitting position are not at all feasible in the beginning. Although the classic sitting postures are the most balanced and scientific postures for supporting the back while sitting, the muscles are usually not strong enough to maintain the asana for more than a few minutes. Yoga nidra is therefore the first choice because it is practised lying on the back in shavasana. Where necessary, extra support may be provided with appropriately placed bolsters or thin cushions. Yoga nidra has further advantages in that it is suitable for beginners, adjustable in duration and may be slotted into existing routines with little restriction as to diet and timings.

Timings

Although the body is more stiff in the morning after sleep, it is precisely at this time that we most appreciate the benefits of our asanas. To overcome the initial early morning stiffness and therefore avoid undue strain, begin your practice only after taking a bath and moving around for a while. Women who are in the house during the day may prefer to practise in the mid-morning before lunch. A second, brief, practice may be undertaken in the evening to eliminate those tensions and pains which have accumulated during the day. Many people find that it is more satisfying to practise yoga nidra in the evening to dispel the day's stress and fatigue.

Wider significance

All yogasanas have some influence on the spine, and the classical meditative postures like siddhasana, padmasana and swastikasana have been evolved for maximum spinal support and comfort while sitting for hours together. Yoga has always put tremendous emphasis on spinal health as a prerequisite for an unimpeded spiritual life. After all, it is alongside the spine that ida and pingala nadis flow – the vessels of our awareness and vitality. There should also be no impairment to the subtle inner channels of the spinal cord through which kundalini flows along sushumna. The practices that eliminate back and spinal problems should therefore not be seen as mere therapy, to be abandoned when the job is done. These practices are the core of sadhana for those who have back pain, but may also be undertaken with benefit by any sadhaka who wishes to maintain the tool of the body in ideal condition for spiritual advancement.

Practice Program

Lower backpain:
   Asana: Tadasana (10), tiryaka tadasana (10), kati chakrasana (10), shavasana, pawanmuktasana (3/3/3), jhulana lurhakanasana (20), nauka sanchalana (10/10), chakki chalanasana (10/10), ardha bhujangasana or bhujangasana (7–21 breaths), shalabhasana (3 times, holding breath), dhanurasana (7–10 breaths), makarasana (for general relaxation).
   Other: Yoga nidra (30 minutes).
Simple program: (for evenings or immediate relief)
   Asana: Tiryaka tadasana (10), kati chakrasana (10), jhulana lurhakanasana (20–30), chakki chalanasana (10/10), ushtrasana (7–10 breaths), marjariasana (15), shashankasana (no time limit).
   Other: Yoga nidra.

Slipped disc: (initial stages)
   Asana: Uttan tadasana (3/3/3), pawanmuktasana (3/3/3), kandharasana (once only, hold seven breaths), ardha bhujangasana (3 times, hold seven breaths), ardha shalabhasana (3 times each leg, hold as long as comfortable), saral dhanurasana (3 times, hold as long as comfortable), makarasana (for general relaxation), advasana or matsya kridasana (for sleeping)
   Precautions: Avoid all forward bending and crossed-leg asanas (use vajrasana instead). After some months commence the above program for lower back pain.

Sciatica:
   Asana: Practise initially as for slipped disc, then as for lower back pain, adding vyaghrasana after marjariasana.
   Precautions: Avoid crossed-leg asanas (use vajrasana), sarvangasana and halasana, extreme forward bending asanas (e.g. paschimottanasana).

113

Cervical spondylitis:

Asana: Skandha chakra (10/10, repeat in evening), greeva sanchalana (10 times each, repeat in evening), tadasana (10), kati chakrasana (10), jhulana lurhakanasana (20), ushtrasana (7 breaths), marjariasana (15 breaths), pranamasana (25–50 breaths).

Shatkarma: Jala neti daily.

Other: Yoga nidra (30 minutes).

Depression

The most insidious and debilitating illness affecting women is depression and more women suffer from some sort of depression than any other single illness. At community health clinics, private mental hospitals and general hospitals throughout the world, the leading diagnosis for women is some kind of depressive disorder. Statistics clearly show that while men are likely to exhibit aggression and alcohol or drug addiction, women are more likely to suffer from forms of depression.

The symptoms

As a clinical label, *depression* is applied only to extreme cases but, in fact, depression appears in many degrees and myriad forms. Such banal signs as nagging, overweight and premature ageing are the outward indicators of something more than just unhappiness, showing also in chronic irritability, nervousness and tiredness to the point of lassitude. Depression is a dysfunction of the whole being, but women often do not (or will not) recognize this for fear of being regarded as crazy or having their problems dismissed as being merely imagination.

In order to be taken seriously, women unconsciously bring into being physical ills that actually did not exist until they themselves made them exist, as tangible expressions of inner tension. The depressed woman may then legitimately seek help for any of a wide range of symptoms including headache, backache, dizziness, heart palpitation, trembling or perspiring hands, loss of appetite, rheumatism, constipation, insomnia, nightmares and painful menstruation. Although these pains are quite real to the sufferer, doctors are usually at a loss to find the physical origin and no amount of direct medication is effective. The busy doctor diagnoses a case of 'nerves' and hands out platitudes with a prescription for tranquilizers that have proved to be physically and psychologically addictive.

Depressed women are subject to excessive fears and worries, shyness, timidity, lack of self-confidence and feelings of inferiority. They are so constantly on edge that even trivial matters become major crises. A woman in this situation feels that life is too much to handle and will tearfully admit 'I just can't cope'. This is inevitably accompanied by energy-sapping guilt, for she objectively realizes that the circumstances of her life are not so difficult. It seems ridiculous to complain about any one of the niggardly irritations that become so potent in numbers and constancy. The trivial things that get these women down, when put into words sound, even to themselves, petty and silly.

The most characteristic and outstanding sign of this state of mind is tiredness out of all proportion to the physical demands made on the body. Too tired to complete her daily tasks, the depressed woman finds that the more 'rest' she takes the more tired she becomes. She is overwhelmed by physical, emotional and mental exhaustion and sinks into a feeling of lifelessness.

Causes

We may experience depression as the aftermath of emotional shock or loss, because of internal biological imbalances or as a disastrous side-effect of drugs prescribed for other illness. Since mind and body are one, in most cases the first two factors are found in combination, aggravating each other and prolonging dark times.

116

Drug induced depression: Many people have felt that depression resulting from drugs could only apply to 'addicts' and not to themselves. It is widely known, for instance, that depression is an after-effect of amphetamine abuse or excessive consumption of alcohol ('hangover' and 'alcoholic's remorse'). However, many drugs legally prescribed for common illnesses may also give rise to depression. These include medication for arthritis, urinary infection, dysentery and digestive infections, and most remedies prescribed for high blood pressure.

Women need especially to be aware that depression is a common side effect of certain oral contraceptive pills, and appetite suppressants frequently used to speed weight reduction. Certain anti-anxiety preparations and sedatives may also cause depression, and if you are taking such prescriptions you must at all times avoid alcohol.

Reactive depression: The name given to prolonged disturbance after an emotional shock or bereavement. Grief for the loss of someone close, or after some calamity, may bring on a depression for two or three months. This is considered normal, but continued intense grieving, despair or apathy persisting beyond this time indicates a much more severe situation. Most often some sudden or unexpected failure can leave us crushed for months – academic failure, the collapse of a business, the break-up of a marriage. Those who suffer from serious physical disabilities might find themselves sinking under the weight of their helplessness and dependence. Although such depressions are considered natural, the depth of our misery here is a measure of the strength of our attachments, and our upliftment depends on the insights that foster vairagya.

Endogenous depression: This arises not from external, but from internal sources, and frequently has a biological component. Depression is a symptom of some type of illness (for example, electrolyte imbalance) and follows in the wake of others, notably influenza and hepatitis. Women, especially, should be aware that depression is frequently associated

117

with anaemia, and often appears after childbirth (usually for a brief period only).

Imbalances in the glandular system also predispose women to depression, especially in relation to pituitary, thyroid and reproductive hormones. An overactive thyroid gland, for instance, will make it difficult for you to sleep, you will be unusually jumpy and prone to anger. An underactive thyroid will deprive you of all your energy and emotional stamina, leaving you lethargic, irritable and vulnerable. Many women experience 'pre-menstrual blues' for ten days to a week before their periods, as a result of imbalance in the hormones of the reproductive cycle. Susceptibility to depression during menopause may be related in part, to erratic and rapidly changing hormonal levels. Where depression has a biological component, the practices of hatha yoga and asana are have been found to be extremely effective in rectifying the situation.

Not so simple

However, the situation is not so simple as it might appear from this analysis. The body affects the mind, but the mind influences the pranas that maintain the body. Hormonal imbalance might make us susceptible to seasons of grey days, but long term dissatisfaction with life, years of unrelenting frustration, may filter down into the body and manifest as physical disturbance. Depression is not always a case of biology distorting the mind. Emotional suppressions, limitations that seemingly can neither be accepted nor transcended can be the root of chronic mental unrest that unsettles the natural functioning of prana and ultimately disrupts the body. This in turn aggravates and perpetuates negative states of mind.

Deviated energy

It is a scientific maxim that energy is neither created nor destroyed, it is only transformed or rechannelled. To yogis it is known that the whole universe is vibrating energy in different forms. Destruction and creation take place when energy is converted from one form to another. Matter and consciousness, for example, are the outcomes of directing energy along two different channels.

Energy as prana is the very stuff of our environment. To the yogic seer, a human being is radiant with the prana flowing along the countless psychic pathways that permeate our entire organism. Kirlian photographs of human bioenergy fields show tiny tongues of 'flame' flaring from the pores with the ebb and flow of the pranic life-force.

To the yogi, mind is also energy. Manomaya kosha and vijnanamaya kosha, which comprise the mental sheaths of mankind, are informed and vitalized by subtle energy. We are energy materialized and when this energy is withdrawn the body dies. Thus, when someone suffering from depression claims to feel lifeless, we can see that the problem really concerns the generation and expression of the energies that constitute our being. Depression is not so much a condition of having no energy, as a kind of psychic constipation blocking our energy flow. The normal pathways become polluted and dammed up so that one is unable to use the energy that is available. Cut off from their usual objects and work, a woman's energies are turned in on herself, giving rise to feelings of emptiness and chaos.

The psychological view
Many psychologists also subscribe to a dynamic energy model of mind. For Freud, the motivating force behind all human activity is the libido, or sexual energy. He conceived of mind as manifesting on two main levels – the conscious and the unconscious. The conscious mind is the rational, objective state which governs our waking lives, regulating the fulfilment of our needs and desires.

The unconscious mind is the storehouse of accumulated energy that seeks expression in the form of instinctive desires or drives. If any of these drives are frustrated, the energy behind it is deflected back into the unconscious mind where it may be rechannelled for expression in a different way. For example, sexual energy may be transformed into creative or spiritual energy. However, if some alternative mode of expression is not available, this becomes a destructive force. The unconscious mind also contains the memory of all past experiences. Any experiences that are particularly painful are pushed deep into the unconscious where a great deal of energy is spent on keeping them beyond remembrance. This repression is both a perversion and a waste of energy for such experiences still make themselves felt in the form of fears and obsessions. It is this turmoil and competition in the unconscious that gives rise to our inner tension.

Wilhelm Reich pointed out that the checks and balances of the mind's energy were reflected in the body and that repression was expressed in psychophysical knots that he called 'muscle armour' and yogis call *granthis*. Although originally a defensive device to protect sensitive areas of the mind from further hurt, these knots are a kind of tourniquet, cutting the healthy flow of energy and blocking us off from whole sections of our being. Sensation is numbed and we become increasingly depleted persons.

Freud considered mankind's basic energy to be primarily sexual and repressed sexuality as the basis of depression and neurosis. Reich was aware that our vitality arises from a more expansive bioenergy, but felt that the inability to surrender to this energy in joyous sexual activity was a major source of inner blocks and tension.

Yogis know that the kundalini shakti that brings transcendental bliss is initially expressed in the gross form as sexual energy. Although yogis transmute and refine this energy for spiritual purposes, they know that it cannot be sublimated from the repressed state. We must be able to find pleasure in sexual expression before we can control and redirect this tremendous energy. This is why the ancient texts say that it is better to practise celibacy only after one has experienced life as a householder. If sexuality is prematurely denied it becomes a destructive force.

It is not surprising, then, to find that the majority of women suffering from depression also have sexual problems. Whatever the source of these problems, it remains that denial or impairment of her sexuality deflects a woman's energy into a system of repression, consuming energy that might otherwise be directed elsewhere. If sexual energy has been properly and systematically redirected into other modes of expression, it greatly enhances vitality and creativity. However, if it is simply pushed out of mind, if it remains an issue of unresolved conflict, it becomes a drain on our resources. Becoming at ease with herself as a sexual creature is one of the necessary steps a woman must take to release herself from depression.

Meaninglessness

However, depression is first and foremost a response to lack of meaning in one's life and we must not make the mistake of defining a woman's life purpose solely in terms of her sexuality. It is this error, this failure to acknowledge the full complexity of womanly being, that has contributed so much to feminine misery.

It is revealing that most of the women seeking psychiatric help for depression are between twenty-one and forty-four years old, that is, in the prime of their lives. It is during these years that their creative energies should be at a peak, that life should be vibrant with the joy of achievement and personal growth. Girls grow into women with the image of happy wife and motherhood before them and, of course, the majority marry and have children. It is precisely at this time of homemaking and childbearing that women expect to find the fulfilment of their life's purpose. Home and children are presented, if not as the only contribution, then as a woman's most significant contribution to life, the proper expression of her creativity and life's work. At a time when the forces of life should be at their strongest and her activities most rewarding, the depressed woman finds her energies turned back against herself in an agony of lifelessness. This is all the more crushing because, according to the popular feminine ideal, she has everything she could want. Nevertheless, the feeling is primarily that something is missing, that life, after all, lacks meaning.

Frustrated creativity

Difficulty arises here because of the current restrictive definition of woman's role in life. Her mode of being is defined only in terms of her biology – mate and mother – and for many women this is not enough. Particularly after children reach school age, many women find that the household is not sufficiently interesting or demanding.

Menial tasks must be done, but they cannot be seen as totally satisfying. A large amount of creativity can be spent, for example, on cooking a meal but it is gobbled down by a blasé family in five minutes – the achievement is not only ephemeral but frequently taken for granted. Likewise with cleaning; as soon as it is finished it must be done again; 'a housewife's work is never done'.

The only approved activities outside the home, more often than not, boil down to doing more housework for someone else – making cakes for stalls, serving in school canteens, cleaning and decorating halls for functions – and committee meetings over tea and biscuits. Although in industrialized countries women can work after marriage, the majority who do so are employed in semi-skilled factory jobs or domestic service. At least these activities are some opportunity to broaden one's sphere, but it is not surprising that women are asking, "Is that all there is?"

Women's depression is creativity turned in on itself by constant frustration. This energy is destructive as it is deprived of scope for expression. Women feel conflict because they are taught that they should exercise their mind and emotions within the family, not against the challenges of the outside world. It is emphasized that they should properly be putting all their energies into supporting the growth of husband and children rather than their own development.

122

That there might be some middle path enabling a woman to combine her home life with full development of her creative potential is also outside the general scope of femininity.

The popular male ideal includes within it the scope for men to be adventurous boundary breakers. For a man to flaunt social convention is not really unconventional. It is, in fact, expected that men should be rebels and explorers of new possibilities. The pioneers and heroes are men, no matter what their field. Men are being truly unconventional only when they begin to develop the 'feminine' side of their natures or to adopt feminine roles. The man who prefers to stay at home and mind the children while his wife works is looked down upon and ridiculed, especially by other men.

On the other hand, the feminine stereotype does not incorporate any allowance for 'radicalism'. A woman who merely steps from what is conventionally 'feminine' to what is still conventional but designated 'masculine' meets with the same hostility as a man who flaunts some of his society's most cherished beliefs. A woman who is not satisfied with the roles of wife and mother is led to believe that the fault must be with herself rather than the fashionable ideal.

If a woman rejects the feminine ideal she meets with difficulty, but if she lives by it completely she is not necessarily saved, for the women who become depressed in middle age are usually the ones who had most fully accepted the traditional feminine role. Devoting themselves totally to being perfect wives and mothers, they reach a stage where this role is no longer needed. The children grow up and become independent; the marital relationship is often tenuous after years of being given second place in favour of the children. Having spent their whole lives in the service of the family only, these women now find themselves redundant.

Since it is female conditioning to contain such conflicts rather than aggressively act them out, women block off their unexpressed energies and sink into depression. Depression can lead to suicide, and throughout the developed world suicide attempters are overwhelmingly female. It has been seen that over two-thirds of suicide attempts in western countries are made by women. Fortunately, most women attempting suicide are not successful. In fact, most of them do not want to die. More often these women are crying out for help; they want someone to realize their plight.

Yoga therapy

In tantric cosmology there are seven *talas* or nether worlds which are symbols for depressed states of consciousness. Yoga is the means to resurrect ourselves from this living death and attain the seven *lokas*, or heavens, which are the progressive states of higher consciousness, potential in everyone. Yoga offers not only relief from tension and renewal of energy, but also a meaning and purpose in the pursuit of higher consciousness. The first step in overcoming depression is to lift the mood of despondency and set natural energies flowing again. For this the practices of hatha yoga are immediate in their efficacy.

Shatkarmas: Kunjal kriya acts as a kind of very mild 'shock therapy' sending a rush of energy into the head and invigorating the whole metabolism. Dullness and a heavy head are removed by the practice of jala neti, which in the case of severe depression should be practised with cold (room temperature) water. Heaviness of heart is often reflected in an exaggerated feeling of heaviness in the body and this is counteracted by shankhaprakshalana. These three kriyas remove tamas, physical sluggishness, remove energy blocks and bring a welcome feeling of lightness to the whole body and mind.

Asanas: These kriyas are supplemented by asanas to rectify hormonal disturbances, to reconnect mind and body and to disperse the psychophysiological armour that inhibits the free movement of energy. Such a program would include dynamic asanas such as naukasanchalana, chakki chalan-asana and surya namaskara, followed by a sequence of asanas that influences each major hormonal gland and chakra. Backward bending and inverted asanas are given special emphasis. One should practise sarvangasana and, if not sirshasana itself, then one of its simpler forms (pranamasana, bhumi pada mastakasana, sirshasana stage one).

Some women with depression feel worse in the morning and brighter towards evening, and they, particularly, will benefit from a full program of kriyas and asanas in the morning. Women who feel brighter in the morning and upset towards evening should also practise the kriyas in the morning, but their asanas should be practised in the late afternoon or early evening.

Pranayama and bandhas: These help to balance swings in mood, and may be practised after asanas, or independently. Kapalbhati, bhastrika and nadi shodhana pranayama are recommended here. Moola bandha should be practised extensively, both in the simple form (rapid contractions) and with the breath. As proficiency increases, up to twelve rounds of maha bandha (moola, uddiyana and jalandhara together) should be practised both morning and evening. Bandhas particularly break through energy barriers, providing access to jammed up vitality and ensuring proper distribution of prana through the chakras.

Meditation: When we are truly depressed – not just sad or out of sorts – conditions are not conducive to meditation. In the beginning, attempts to meditate are attempts to escape rather than confront our difficulties. When the outer life is aimless and confused, this confusion and aimlessness befogs our attempts to look within. There is no clarity and we either drift into sleep or fall victim to the usual cycle of frustrated thinking. In this way, much time is consumed and nothing constructive is achieved.

However, as the asanas, kriyas and bandhas take effect, our mood lightens, courage and clarity begin to surface. Eventually meditation becomes essential to remove deep seated samskaras that are the root of negative patterns of reaction, and to develop an understanding of our true nature that will be our inner guide and inspiration for living a full and satisfying life.

Meditation is also psychotherapy, giving us periods of calmness and clarity that enable us to take a more realistic look at life. We see situations in a new light, helping us to bring change in our lives. We see more clearly the elements that cause disruption, and work out new ways of coming to terms with our limitations and aspirations. With new insight and expanded awareness, life begins to show fresh promise, greater meaning begins to flower.

One very direct method of releasing oppressive mental tension is antar mouna, the practice of inner silence. Antar mouna first increases resistance to external disturbances, then awareness is gradually drawn inward, and unconscious thoughts and pent-up emotion slowly emerge into conscious perception. Buffered by a state of relaxation, we become aware of thoughts, feelings, desires and frustrations that have been denied or hidden for years. These are gradually acknowledged by the waking mind and the energy that was used in burying them is now freed for better purposes.

Eventually a stage is reached where thoughts and emotions from the deeper mind lose their power over us, and at this stage the thought processes can be controlled to induce a state of thoughtlessness. This spontaneously leads to a state of meditation and contact with the core of our being, the real self. This contact, more than anything else in life, transforms one's whole understanding of existence and gives our life its power and significance.

Yogic routine
Yogis live by a schedule of sleeping, eating, working and meditating that takes maximum advantage of the natural energy cycles of body and mind. A similar routine will reinforce yoga practices and help to accelerate the recovery from depression.

Sleep: A depressed woman feels that she has no vitality and that she must take numerous rest periods to maintain the little energy she does have. In many cases, women find the oblivion of sleep an addictive relief from their problems.

They begin to sleep more and more, not from physical need, but as an escape from grey reality. Eight hours sleep a day is adequate for the average person, six is optimum, and less is required as we move beyond middle-age. Too much sleep is exhausting, slowing the body processes and dulling the mind; too much sleep leads to a build up of tamas with its associated feelings of negativity. In cases of depression, not more sleep but less is needed. Try to resist over sleeping and do not sleep during the day. If you feel sleepy, take a cold shower – it will leave you feeling more energetic and more positive. Sleeping a maximum of six to eight hours will refresh both body and mind, and make more time available for sadhana and other activities.

'Early to bed and early to rise makes a woman healthy, wealthy and wise.' This homely advice is also an important maxim in yogic life. We enjoy our most refreshing sleep before midnight, so by going to bed early we gain more benefit from each hour of slumber. This also enables us to wake in time to take advantage of brahmamuhurta, the period of heightened consciousness (literally 'Brahman hour'), between four and six in the morning. Being awake at this time takes advantage of hormonal changes which take place around 4 a.m. This is a time when the forces of the universe are in sattwic harmony, enabling us to tune in more easily with the inner self and the powers of the cosmos.

If you make a habit of getting up early in the morning you will find it has a great effect on your life. However, the condition is that you must be strict in following this routine. At first it will require effort and organization, but later it will become a pleasure to rise early. Begin with a bath or shower, preferably in cold water, then some light physical activity to shake off sleep. Surya namaskara is ideal, or a few asanas, but if you can not manage this then do a little household cleaning. Then sit for meditation and you will find the mind naturally more calm, more introvert. It is for this reason that yogis recommend this time above all others as ideal for spiritual practices.

Many famous thinkers, writers, painters and other creative people have also commented that they find this their most productive time, the time when ideas and inspiration flow most freely. If you wish to develop some talent, to cultivate some means of creative expression, then this is the time to practise. If you do not feel inclined to any of these things, just begin your daily duties and you will undoubtedly receive some inspiration as to how to make the most valuable use of this time. This one routine will enable you to awaken all your talent potentialities and may be practised as a sadhana in itself. At the very least it is valuable therapy, and you will find that you have more energy and optimism to rise above your depression.

Food: Another means of compensating for misery is to find pleasure in eating more. Although some people eat less when depressed, most depressed women overeat in general, and particularly crave sweets. Too much sweet not only puts on weight and upsets the physical metabolism, but also allows dullness and tamas to predominate. You will never fill up that inner emptiness with food, and you will further deplete your energies through unnecessary guilt. Eat on time, do not eat between meals, and avoid too many sweets.

Karma yoga

Energy is not lost by exertion. Rather, meaningful activity generates more energy and power. To counteract depression we have to abandon brooding and find something to do instead. Just as we have to re-educate atrophied muscles after a long illness, we must reopen energy pathways clogged by depression. Energy must be redirected outwards in some form, any form, of activity in order to short-circuit the system of repression. In yoga it is known that sattwic harmony can only emerge after the inertia of tamoguna has been overcome by rajasic activity. To overcome depression, energy must be redeployed in movement and creation. At first this is harder than it sounds, but start by setting yourself some goal and begin working towards it in small steps. For instance, you might begin to practise asanas for just five minutes daily, maybe just one asana. After a few days, add another and lengthen your practice time. By setting small goals, you will be less likely to be discouraged and every success, no matter how small, makes you stronger. Every step takes you closer to your goal and every goal achieved adds to confidence and a sense of well-being.

To keep discouragement at bay, we must abandon the past and resist expectations of the future. Even the most mundane activities take on greater significance when we give our full attention to the present – just here, right now. When you do anything – eating, sweeping the floor, feeding the baby – try not to think of anything else, especially not what comes after you have finished. Relax into the action as if at this moment you have nothing else in this world you would rather do, and you will find enjoyment along with the recognition that every mindful action is a creative expression of your individual existence.

Take some help

When she is depressed, a woman is very likely to claim that she has no time for extra activities – especially yoga sadhana. When one is sunk in apathy, there is no motivation to do anything, nothing has any appeal. Moreover, it is difficult to muster willpower because our internal resources are scattered and dissipated. At such a time, we can take the help of someone close to provide the momentum we need. Do not be ashamed to call on your family or a friend to share their energy and willpower by calling you in the morning, working with you occasionally, reminding you of your sadhana schedule. You know yourself that often your feelings will be mixed, and that from time to time you will resent the constant prodding, that you might even lose your temper with those who are trying to help. If your supporters are wise, they will encourage you just to pick up and carry on, and if you persist, soon you will have built up enough energy to manage on your own.

Staying for some time in a yogashram is ideal, and might be necessary for the severely depressed. Ashram life will automatically set you on a new schedule of early rising, correct eating, karma yoga. You will have a change from the circumstances that are getting you down, and a chance to find a new perspective while learning the recommended yoga practices.

Reconditioning

The worst aspect of depression is the sense of helplessness, that we must simply endure, and cannot of our own accord transcend our moods and feelings. The greatest contribution of yoga is the assurance that we can help ourselves, and need no longer be passive victims. If you are prone to depression, you must face the fact that your moods and energies are going to sink from time to time, but if you make yoga a part of your life you will be able to take concrete steps to minimize the impact of dark days and more rapidly restore a balance. Regular practise of yoga will maintain an inner stability that is less vulnerable to emotional upset, and provide the experiences from which we can develop a constructive philosophy for managing difficulties.

Depression will only finally be overcome when we develop a full knowledge of our own emotional dynamics, and break down the conditioning that determines our reactions to things around us. Our yoga practices provide a basis for witnessing our thoughts and actions without becoming painfully ensnared in them. *Sakshi bhava*, the attitude of impartial awareness of all we do, is not the painful alienation of depression; it is a state in which there is no judgement, no emotional identification with our thoughts and feelings. There is simply detached acknowledgement. Such an attitude acts as a kind of ballast during emotional storms, and brings self-knowledge, peace and harmony. Instead of identifying with our weaknesses, we act from a point of strength.

Women must examine themselves and unflinchingly identify their greatest needs, desires and talents, regardless of whether or not they are traditionally 'feminine'. They must then become aware of their conditioned attitudes towards themselves and how these attitudes work to limit their happiness and effectiveness in the world. The notion of living up to some external standard must be replaced by a self-regulating principle based on self-knowledge. Yoga provides women with the means of achieving this essential knowledge of themselves and integrating it in harmonious self-acceptance. Yoga unifies the mind, generating new willpower. It unleashes the energies by which a woman is released into new vigour, providing the means to realize her highest visions.

Headache

Headache is one of woman's most common discomforts and one of her most common excuses: "Oh I can't, I have a headache" or, "Don't make any noise, mummy has a headache". Headache can be of various kinds resulting from tension, sinusitis, high blood pressure, eye strain, digestive upsets and tumour (rarely).

Hormonal imbalance

Doctors have noticed that the majority of headache patients are women, and almost two thirds of migraine sufferers are women. This suggests that there might be a physical base in a woman's constitution that acts as a predisposing factor. Some women experience headache as part of the syndrome of pre-menstrual tension (congestive dysmenorrhoea) or during menopause. For many other women who suffer frequent or recurring headache, there is often a link with the menstrual cycle – headaches occurring more often in the middle of the cycle (around ovulation time) and/or at the end of the cycle (just prior to menstruation).

It is doubtful that the headache is directly due to the changing chemical balance of the body. However it would seem that the fluctuation in hormonal levels renders some women more vulnerable to physical and emotional stress and it is well known that emotional upset is the major precipitating factor in all headaches.

Tension headache

Stress or tension may take many forms, and is the major cause of all headaches. Given an underlying physical predisposition, headache is usually triggered by some sort of emotional upset. Depression, excessive worrying, a too tense attitude to work, chronic frustration and dissatisfaction are all major factors in tension headaches.

Some women will notice an early warning of impending headache when they become irritable and snappy, others find they cry a lot before and after the headache begins. These sick headaches, with their accompanying lethargy and intolerance, are very often the concrete expression of a woman's dissatisfaction with her life and herself. No amount of pampering or medication is going to eliminate headaches of this kind, and such women need to find a new perspective on, and more satisfying basis for their lives through a thorough involvement in yoga.

Migraine headache

Migraine is the most severe kind of headache disorder and is due to disturbances in the widening and narrowing of the blood vessels in the head. This is controlled by the autonomic nervous system, and such fluctuations in the blood vessels are efforts of the nervous system to compensate for excessive emotional tension. A migraine is characterized by pain on one side of the head, and lasts for up to three days. It is frequently accompanied by a sick feeling that may last for several hours before causing vomiting. Women with migraines might see flashes, spots or lines before the eyes, and usually find bright light and loud noises intolerable.

Constitutional factors

There is evidence to suggest that a tendency to migraines can be inherited, and it is fairly well established that many who suffer from migraine complained as children of travel sickness and unexplained, recurrent pains in the abdomen. Migraine itself usually begins around the time of puberty,

133

and less often in later life. Since many more women than men suffer from migraines, this suggests that the variations in a woman's hormonal cycle might have a part to play in the problem. Regular practice of a balanced asana program goes a long way to compensate for these basic physical tendencies. Surya namaskara, bhujangasana, dhanurasana, pranamasana and sarvangasana are all recommended.

Diet

Some people are constitutionally sensitive to certain chemicals and foods which may precipitate a kind of allergic headache. This is often overlooked, for the foods in question are commonly eaten by many people without adverse reaction. However, it is now well established that certain foods must be avoided by those who have a tendency to migraine. This includes chocolate, cocoa, cola, pork, eggs, seafoods (fish and shellfish like oysters), and alcohol (especially beer). For some people fried foods, butter, milk and coffee must be added to this list, and for others even lemons, oranges, and tomatoes (all highly acid) are suspect.

In relation to yoga therapy many people have found relief by combining shankhaprakshalana (intestinal washing) with a simpler diet. A vegetarian diet seems most helpful, with plenty of grains (wheat, rice, ragi, barley), dal, and a variety of fruits and vegetables.

Emotional factors

Observations indicate that people who suffer from migraine tend to be intelligent, but are also inclined to be obsessional in their approach to life. Often they are fussy and demanding, and find it difficult to tolerate shortcomings in themselves and others. This is frequently accentuated by excessive fear and worrying, or constant frustration.

Systematic relaxation through yoga nidra will release accumulated tension before it brings on a headache, and working in the spirit of karma yoga develops a more relaxed and tolerant outlook.

134

Yoga therapy

Yoga therapy for migraine will include jala neti, kunjal kriya and yoga nidra, together with a systematic program of asanas. These practices should be undertaken according to the schedule suggested by a competent yoga therapist, and they may be applied at the time headache is threatening.

Usually there will be some warning that a headache is developing, and jala neti and yoga nidra at the very outset can be enough to prevent its full development. Neti not only washes the nose but also has a soothing influence on the nerves of the face and head. Where headache has set in, it is often relieved by vomiting, so kunjal kriya should be practised at the earliest opportunity. This may even be done some time after meals (vyaghra kriya) and it is far better to practise kunjal kriya than to suffer unnecessarily with hours of nausea. It is this prolonged nausea that causes a large part of the weakness associated with tension headache.

Other headaches

All that has been said about the emotional factors in migraine headache also applies to any other kind of headache, including those due to eye strain, sinusitis and high blood pressure. Any existing physical problem will be aggravated by tension. Yoga nidra or some other form of meditation should therefore be a common factor in any therapy schedule which should not stop at mere therapy, but should also be an introduction to a more constructive yogic philosophy.

Sinus headache

Along with a blocked or runny nose, there is often a feeling of heaviness or stuffiness in the head due to inflammation of the sinus passages above and below the eyes. At times this intensifies into a distinct aching or pain that becomes more acute when you sneeze, cough, or bend forward. To relieve this headache it is necessary to clear up the mucus blockage of the nose, to empty the sinuses of congestion and soothe the membranes of the nasal and sinus passages.

Neti: The most relevant practices here are the various forms of nose washing, called neti. Jala neti is the process of rinsing the nose with warm, salty water by pouring water in one nostril and out the other. The nose is then thoroughly dried by a special breathing process. When practising jala neti for sinusitis, particular attention must be given to postural drainage after the practice for at least one minute, and perhaps up to three minutes, depending on your individual condition. Jala neti should be practised daily, and may be practised two or three times a day where congestion is severe. After a few days of this, once daily will be sufficient to keep the nose clear.

From the colour and odour of the nasal mucus you can determine whether or not infection is present. If there is infection, practise swamutra neti. The process is the same as for jala neti, but instead of plain salty water, you use your own urine, collected on the first urination of the morning. Chronic and persistent blockage might also require the practice of sutra neti. Here a waxed thread or rubber catheter is passed in through one nostril and out through the mouth.

All these practices must be learned under the supervision of an experienced teacher, who will also indicate when and how often you should practise according to individual needs.

Asana and pranayama: Neti should be supplemented by a brief program of asana and pranayama. A few rounds of surya namaskara will open a blocked nose and backward bending asanas enhance the effect. Avoid inverted asanas until congestion clears. Of the pranayamas, bhastrika with both nostrils open and nadi shodhana are most important.

Diet: Eating early at night (before 7.00 p.m.) is a great help in reducing mucus congestion. At night avoid eating heavy foods, fried or oily food, and milk products (cheese, milk, curd, buttermilk). Avoid processed foods, white flour products and refined white rice. At other meals take your normal diet, but minimize milk products as much as possible, and take plenty of vegetables.

136

Digestive headache

Headaches that begin an hour or so after meals may be related to improper digestion. Such headaches are often accompanied by a sense of fullness or discomfort in the stomach or abdomen, and occasionally by puffiness of face or eyes. Acidity and constipation are both precursors of this kind of headache.

Diet: A simple diet, without much oil or ghee. Plenty of vegetables and lots of plain water are also helpful. A vegetarian diet is best.

Yoga therapy: Practise kunjal kriya and laghoo shankha-prakshalana on alternate days for two weeks, then gradually reduce to a routine of laghoo shankhaprakshalana once a week and kunjal kriya once a week (not on the same day). Jala neti should be practised daily, together with asanas that improve the digestion. Avoid inverted asanas for the first few weeks.

Eye strain

If you suspect eye strain is the cause of your headache, first consult a competent doctor. In addition to his recommendations, practise jala neti and eye exercises daily. Nadi shodhana and inverted asanas are also helpful. Learning to use the eyes efficiently without strain is encouraged by daily practise of trataka. Trataka is steady, relaxed gazing at any object, and in this case, a flame fed by castor oil is recommended. Trataka concurrently develops concentration, and results in a relaxed state of real well-being.

Practice between headaches

Do not postpone your yoga practice until you have developed a headache. Although neti and yoga nidra are often sufficient to relieve an oncoming headache, regular daily practice is required to prevent the problem altogether. Daily practice of yoga will help to overcome headache in two ways: first by reducing the intensity of symptoms, and secondly by increasing the time interval between attacks until they

137

disappear completely. At the very least, yoga will compensate for the constitutional and emotional factors that lead to headache, and ultimately it has the potential to transform your life from one of oppression to one of inspiration.

Practice program

Migraine:

Asana: Surya namaskara (3–6 rounds), shavasana, vajrasana (1 minute), supta vajrasana (one minute) marjariasana (15), shashankasana (2–3 minutes), pranamasana (3 minutes), shavasana.
Pranayama: Nadi shodhana pranayama (10 rounds).
Shaktkarma: Laghoo shankhaprakshalana (twice weekly for one month then once a week), kunjal kriya (daily for one week then twice a week), jala neti (daily).
Other: Yoga nidra (30–45 minutes).
Diet: Careful.

Acute headache:

Asana: Pranamasana (3–5 minutes).
Shaktkarma: Kunjal kriya (even if the stomach is not empty), jala neti, laghoo shankhaprakshalana (next morning).
Other: Yoga nidra.

Sinusitis:

Asana: Surya namaskara (6 rounds), shavasana, kandharasana (1 minute), bhujangasana (1 minute), dhanurasana (30 seconds), paschimottanasana (2 minutes).
Pranayama: Bhastrika pranayama (5 rounds), nadi shodhana pranayama (10–20 rounds), jala neti (daily), sutra neti (twice a week).
Other: Yoga nidra (30 minutes).
Diet: Careful.

Digestive headache:

Asana: Naukasana (5), pawanmuktasana (5 each side), jhulana lurhakanasana (20), chakki chalanasana (10 each way), ushtrasana (1 minute), marjariasana (15 times), vajrasana (after meals).

Pranayama: Bhastrika pranayama (5 rounds).

Shaktkarma: Agnisar kriya (50 rounds), jala neti (daily), kunjal kriya (alternate days for two weeks then once a week), laghoo shankhaprakshalana (alternate days for two weeks then once a week).

Other: Yoga nidra (30 minutes).

Diet: Careful.

Leucorrhoea

Modesty has traditionally and universally been praised as a virtue of womanhood, and no woman secure in her sensitivity and inner poise would deny it. Yet it is false modesty that is rooted in fear and ignorance. For too long, women have been victims of myth, ignorance and confusion concerning their bodies. There is no conflict between modesty and frankness, and it is frankness that we need to sweep away the webs of superstition and to restore the confidence in our physical selves that is the basis of true womanliness.

No one will appreciate this more than the many women who have, at some time or other, sought advice about the specifically feminine problem of leucorrhoea or excessive vaginal discharge. From sheer lack of information and openness, many women are worried, ashamed and afraid of this essentially simple and manageable disorder.

What's natural

To begin with, many women think they have leucorrhoea when in fact they do not. It must be understood that a certain amount of vaginal secretion is normal and healthy. The walls of the vagina contain many tiny glands whose specific function is continually to produce a cleansing and lubricating film of moisture. This secretion acts as protection for the sensitive tissues of the vagina, preventing them from drying up and washing out any undesirable microbes. The

140

vagina, like the eye, is self-cleansing. Just as the eye is bathed with moisture at every blink, so too the vagina is kept fresh by the constant flow of internal secretion.

Healthy vaginal discharge is usually transparent or slightly milky, and may be a little slippery. However, the texture varies with the phases of the menstrual cycle. Sometimes it is thin and watery, other times it is very white, and quite thick and sticky like jelly. The amount of secretion also varies from time to time and woman to woman. It may become noticeable even in young girls before puberty. If the vagina is healthy, there is no smell and no irritation or redness of the vagina and surrounding area.

Not to be confused with infections
Extremely heavy vaginal secretion is a sign of imbalance, but is definitely not an infection. Just the same, it does create an excessively moist condition that is ideal for the development of vaginal infections.

As there are bacteria on the skin, in the mouth and in the intestines, so too there are many bacteria present in the normal, healthy vagina. Some of these are friendly bacteria that keep the vaginal environment slightly acid, and so prevent the excessive growth of potentially harmful organisms. At times, however, this natural balance is disrupted and infections develop. Vaginal infections though, are not to be confused with leucorrhoea. In the case of infection, there is not only abnormal discharge, but also mild or severe itching, burning of the area around the vagina (vulva). There is irritation of the vagina itself and, occasionally, more frequent urination. The first signs of infection are lower back pain, cramps and swelling of the glands in the thighs and abdomen.

The main index of infection is the nature of the discharge itself. Irregular discharges referred to as 'non-specific vaginitis' mean that infection is present but doctors do not know what it is. The discharge may be white, yellow or streaked with blood. In some cases the walls of the vagina

141

can be puffy with fluid or covered with a thick coat of pus. However, the two most common sources of infection are monilia and trichomonas, both of which are normally present in the healthy body.

With monilia or yeast infections, the discharge is thick and white, and may look like cottage cheese or curd. It has a smell like baking bread, and this negative association can make a woman feel sick at the mere smell of food. Monilia infections are also very itchy and irritating to the whole vagina and vulva.

Trichomonas is present in both men and women, and about fifty percent of women have this organism in their vagina, but often without any discomfort. When the trichomonas population grows too large, it gives a thin, foamy discharge of yellowish-green or grey and is identified by an extremely unpleasant odour. It often flares up after intercourse, due to irritation of the vagina, and can also be passed on by wet towels, underwear or dirty toilet seats.

Vaginal infections are extremely common. It is a rare woman who does not pick up such an infection at least once in her lifetime. These disorders are not to be classed with such virulent diseases as syphilis or gonorrhoea, and there is absolutely no cause for shame or humiliation. The secrecy and superstition surrounding female sexuality has been known to prevent women from seeking help in the case of infection, and the effects have been disastrous. If treated early, vaginal disorders are a minor nuisance; if neglected they become difficult to cure, may lead to more complicated illnesses and may cause organic damage to the point of infertility. If ignored during pregnancy the baby is also affected.

Failure to take proper measures is both cowardly and dangerous, and you should not compromise your health with mere amulets and stones obtained from unauthorized practitioners with little medical knowledge. They might provide psychological reassurance, but the infection goes on unabated. If you contract a digestive infection that gives you 'excessive anal discharge' in the form of diarrhoea, you

142

are not ashamed and feel it is only normal to consult a doctor. This should also be your attitude to vaginal discharges and other irregularities of the reproductive system. Competent medical help, backed up with preventive yogic practices will ensure relief and rapid recovery.

Leucorrhoea

Between these two poles of normal protective secretion and vaginal infection we have a non-infectious, painless but excessive discharge, and this is leucorrhoea. Leucorrhoea is just like normal vaginal secretion, only much more copious. While regular secretion may leave white or yellowish spots on your underwear, it usually dries quickly and does not cause discomfort. However, if your clothes are marked, if you feel constantly wet or have to change your underwear several times a day, then there is no doubt the discharge is excessive. Some women find it so heavy that they must wear sanitary napkins even between their periods. You might experience pain in the back, chaffing of the thighs, or a 'full' feeling in the abdomen. These are similar to the early indicators of infection, but are less severe. Moreover, infection usually causes more frequent urination and leucorrhoea makes it less. Leucorrhoea is an abnormally profuse discharge, but a clean one, and does not cause any itching or inflammation of the vaginal area.

Predisposing factors

Leucorrhoea can be the first sign of cervical erosion (sores developing on the opening to the womb). It is estimated that about ninety-five percent of women develop such sores at some time during their childbearing years, so it is well worth medical investigation. Generally doctors conduct a full pelvic examination and take a pap smear.

Most often, though, leucorrhoea is just one signal from our bodies that we are generally run-down and our resistance is low, due to lack of sleep, bad diet or nervous tension. Women who have diabetes or TB are particularly susceptible.

143

The next most common cause of excessive discharge is hormonal imbalance. Women using birth control pills or IUDs (loop, copper 7, etc.) are especially prone. It may also become a problem just before or after menstruation, during pregnancy or menopause, because of the natural alteration of hormonal levels at these times.

Diet is an important factor in leucorrhoea. Excess mucus from too much milk, white flour and polished rice is expelled in the form of bodily discharges, including those from the vagina. Highly spiced and fatty food, and large quantities of sugar also contribute to this problem. Diets high in processed sugar and refined carbohydrates create ideal conditions for vaginal infections because they change the acidity level of the vagina and allow harmful bacteria to proliferate. Numerous women have reported that simply adjusting their diet has drastically reduced vaginal discharge.

Leucorrhoea very often occurs in conjunction with constipation which is well known to result not only from faulty diet but also from stress and tension. When we are under constant tension, we can become so accustomed to it that we are not consciously anxious. We think we are relaxed. However, the body registers this and the sympathetic nervous system is activated, moving energy away from the digestive system to speed up heartbeat and so on. Under these conditions, constipation is easily developed. Stress reactions also affect the adrenal glands, and variations in the hormones produced by the adrenals could well be responsible for leucorrhoea, and would account for the link between constipation and excessive discharge.

Other emotional factors can be unconscious. Women have many bad feelings about their physical selves that are hard to admit. So much so, that these negative attitudes may not consciously be acknowledged at all. This is particularly true in connection with the reproductive organs, which are still frequently unmentionable. Such unconscious doubts may be expressed as leucorrhoea, the excess discharge being a symbolic attempt to purify ourselves.

Personal hygiene

Strict personal hygiene is the first step in dealing with leucorrhoea. It not only prevents infection and minimizes discomfort, but also helps to put the mind at rest. Wash the anus and vulva regularly. Pat the vulva dry and try to keep it dry. Many vaginal infections are due to a spill over of organisms from the anus to the vagina, so always wash or wipe the anus from front to back. Use the traditional oriental squatting posture on toilet seats – it is not only more efficient but also more hygienic. Avoid nylon underwear, tights or pantyhose. Nylon retains both moisture and heat, providing a 'hothouse' environment that encourages harmful bacteria. Wear only loose fitting cotton underwear, or when the discharge is not so heavy, none at all. Many undesirable organisms are killed simply by exposure to air, which also freshens and cools the vaginal area.

Yoni prakshalana

Douching or washing the interior of the vagina can be an aid in preventing infection provided it is not overdone. The healthy vagina is rather acid, and this acidity acts as a barrier to infection. Since blood is alkaline, the acidity level (pH) drops during menstruation and we tend to be more prone to infection. At this time douching with a slightly acid solution will re-establish the normal pH and may have a preventive value. Suitable solutions are one teaspoon of bicarbonate of soda to half a litre of warm water, or one teaspoon of vinegar to a litre of warm water. Coating the interior of the vagina and the vulva with curd is also recommended by many women for curing infections. It seems to be effective provided it is applied in the very early stages while the symptoms are mild.

However, even the most exotic douching solution does not help much in cases of leucorrhoea, except that it can be reassuring. We must remember that the vagina is self-cleansing, that leucorrhoea is actually a kind of continual douche. By constantly washing out the vagina with anything

145

other than plain water, we risk disturbing the natural protective mechanisms. Excessive douching acts as a stimulant for already overactive glands, and sets up a marked self-consciousness, both of which only aggravate the problem.

Restoring the balance

The fact remains that the most common causes of leucorrhoea are generally low vitality and hormonal imbalance. For women the two are so intimately linked that they can be seen as simply two different ways of stating the same problem. Since this is the case, yogic practices can benefit in relieving persistently excessive discharge.

Yogasanas are invaluable for strengthening and harmonizing the activity of a woman's whole reproductive system because of their direct influence on the abdominal and pelvic organs, and their regulating effects on the glandular system. A suitable program for leucorrhoea would include surya namaskara, vajrasana, shashankasana, marjariasana and ushtrasana. Sarvangasana and vipareeta karani asana would also have a positive influence, while more advanced practitioners could include bhujangasana, shalabhasana, dhanurasana, chakrasana and paschimottanasana.

Yogic practices have subtle effects on the vital energies that mobilize the body and motivate the mind. Yoga is the science of vital energy, prana shakti and every yoga technique works to enhance our vigour and vitality. For this reason, all the asanas should be held for some time with awareness directed to the appropriate chakra or psychic energy centre.

Practices specifically recommended for restoring vitality are psychic energy manipulations called *bandhas*. The most relevant to leucorrhoea are moola bandha and uddiyana bandha. Pranayamas such as nadi shodhana, bhastrika and ujjayi further enhance vitality and eliminate toxins, while meditative practices like yoga nidra or antar mouna short-circuit the tension that disturbs our hormonal balance and depletes prana shakti. These practices harmonize the body and mind, eliminating the root cause of disorder.

146

Practice program

Leucorrhoea:

    Asana: Surya namaskara (6–12 rounds), shavasana, vajrasana (15 breaths), supta vajrasana (15 breaths), ushtrasana (15 breaths), marjariasana (15 times), shashankasana (30), vipareeta karani asana (twenty-one breaths).

    Pranayama: Ujjayi pranayama (54 rounds).

    Shatkarma: Laghoo shankhaprakshalana (once a week).

    Other: Yoga nidra (half an hour).

Menstrual Irregularities

No woman's menstrual cycle is perfectly regular, for no two occurrences in nature are perfectly identical. Each menses is a unique event within our personal pattern, so there is no need to be alarmed by any small variations we perceive in our monthly cycle. We must not interpret this as evidence of our basic sickness. Only when we notice persistent irregularity, need we begin to think that something might be amiss. There are certain questions that come up again and again, for they reflect events experienced at some time or another by nearly everyone. The following discussion is typical of the questions so often raised, and we have answered them here so that as many women as possible may enjoy the physical health and freedom of spirit that comes with yoga.

Can we practise yoga during our period?

During excessive bleeding asanas should not be practised, and in general, sirshasana and sarvangasana are not practised even if the flow is normal. However, pranayama, meditation and other practices may be continued as usual. In fact, yoga regards this time as a very fruitful one for sadhana. Women are more sensitive and more psychically potent at this time, enhancing the possibility of a breakthrough in spiritual experience. We should therefore give greater emphasis to japa and dhyana at this time in order to take advantage of this natural expansion in inner awareness.

I am a yoga teacher and many women approach me about period problems. What is the most important thing I can tell them?

When a woman comes to her teacher for help with period irregularities – too few, too many, too heavy – the most valuable piece of advice we can give is 'see a doctor immediately.' A full medical examination will clarify the exact nature of this problem which can have so many causes. Period irregularities are often just a sign of some other misfunction or illness which may lead to serious complications if not properly treated. Once the doctor has eliminated this possibility, the student is reassured and the teacher is able to decide on the most appropriate practices for establishing harmony and balance, physically and spiritually.

My daughter is eighteen and she has begun to develop a womanly figure, but still she does not have her periods. I am very worried about this.

Most girls experience *menarche* (first menstruation) about eleven or twelve, but it can occur anytime between nine and eighteen. If your daughter is otherwise healthy, it is possible that she is just a late developer. However, amenorrhoea (absence of menstruation) could be due to defects in the structure of the reproductive system, cysts or tumours, hormonal imbalance or emotional factors associated with growing into her woman's role. If the doctor finds no cause for alarm, she should practise twelve rounds of surya namaskara every morning.

I am only forty-nine years old, but my period seems to have stopped, except for occasional irregular spots or streaks. Surely this is too early for menopause.

The average age for the cessation of periods is forty-eight or forty-nine, but a woman can reach this phase in her life-cycle anytime between forty and fifty-five. As a rough guide, bear in mind that doctors have found women who begin to menstruate early, finish later. However, irregular spotting

149

or 'breakthrough' bleeding between periods could also be due to general infection of the reproductive system (pelvic inflammatory disease) or to polyps (protrusions that grow from the mucous membrane at or near the opening to the womb). If your medical report is clear, then begin yoga practices to harmonize your hormones and minimize any physical discomfort that might come with menopause. Inverted asanas are particularly beneficial, especially, sirshasana (headstand), sarvangasana (shoulder stand) and halasana (plough).

My period normally lasts five days, but for two months it was only for two days and last month it did not come at all. I've also been feeling sick some mornings.

The most common cause of missed periods is pregnancy, and this would seem to be the case if you also have morning sickness. For some women menstruation stops immediately after conception, but for others it may continue for two or three months although the flow is short and scanty. If you are taking birth control pills it could be that they have the wrong combination of hormones for your particular system and are suppressing your periods. After childbirth, menstruation will most likely start again after six weeks or so, unless you are breast feeding the baby. Often while producing mother's milk you will not menstruate. If you have been using the pill and discontinue, your first period will probably not come for about six weeks. If you are pregnant it is already time to begin preparing yourself for a natural and harmonious birth with pranayama and yoga nidra.

I have always had regular periods, but since I left home to go to college my periods have stopped.

Very few women have absolutely regular periods, for many situations in life affect the hormones that govern the cycle. Leaving home for the first time, combined with the extra demands of student life, is a challenge that puts us under a certain degree of emotional strain. This could be enough to

150

stop your periods for a while. Some women are more sensitive in this respect than others, but it is possible for any major change in routine to bring a temporary halt in your periods. This could come about with a long journey, moving from the country to the more hectic pace of the city (or vice versa), a radical change in diet or climate, entering a new occupation, beginning or ending a romance, grief over loss of someone close, beginning married life, or any other intense emotional experience.

Illness – fevers, intestinal upsets, obesity, even serious constipation – can also stop menstruation for some time.

If you have clearance from your doctor, begin regular practise of yoga nidra. This will bring not only physical relaxation, but also deep emotional relaxation and help with your studies. It is likely that you also need more physical exercise, so add to your program dynamic asanas like nauka sanchalana, chakki chalanasana, shashankasana, marjari-asana, shashank-bhujangasana, and druta halasana.

My period comes regularly, but so often! There are usually only twenty-one or twenty-two days between each one. Is something wrong?

Check with your doctor, but do not be too alarmed. The average cycle is twenty-eight days, but your cycle may be as short as twenty or as long as thirty-six and still be normal. If you take up a regular practise of asanas, pranayama and meditation, your cycle may become a little longer.

My period is very heavy and lasts a week. Is this normal?

A normal period can last anywhere from two to eight days, and four to six is average. The usual loss is four to six tablespoons, or two to three ounces. If you have very heavy bleeding, it is important to distinguish between menstrual flow and haemorrhage (bleeding from internal disorders). If the flow comes with a sensation of 'gushing' or 'flooding' then it is possible that the bleeding does not come only from the usual breakdown of the uterine lining.

151

Excessive bleeding could be a symptom of either endometriosis or fibroids. *Endometriosis* takes place when the tissue that normally grows in the uterus grows somewhere else instead – frequently the bladder or intestine. This disorder is quite common in women between thirty and forty, and needs expert attention. Between twenty and twenty-five percent of women develop *fibroids*, which are growths of tough, fibrous tissue in the womb, resulting from incomplete breakdown of the lining. A small percentage of fibroids are cancerous, and this condition can have complications for the bladder and bowel. It is most important, then to seek medical advice in the case of persistent heavy periods.

If medical investigations indicate that your problem is due to hormonal imbalance, then learn antar mouna or yoga nidra from a qualified teacher, along with the following asanas – sarvangasana, halasana, kandharasana, ardha matsyendrasana, bhujangasana, shalabhasana, dhanurasana and paschimottanasana.

Since I have stopped eating meat my periods have stopped too. This has happened to several of my vegetarian friends, but we all feel our health has never been better.

Diet influences every aspect of our physical health, including menstruation, and it is now well-established that high-protein meat diets can cause more pain and heavier blood loss. Often when changing to a vegetarian diet one's periods stop temporarily, but when they come again they are usually trouble-free. Women on a vegan diet (grain and vegetables, no milk or other animal products), may find their periods stop. However, examination of their normal vaginal discharge shows that their hormones are still functioning and there is no loss of femininity. These women still lead an active married life and give birth to healthy, happy babies.

Most commonly however, a strict diet works best to reduce menstruation only when it is combined with absolute chastity, and you and your friends will probably find your period begins again after marriage.

152

Is it normal for periods to stop when one adopts a spiritual life?

There are certain spiritual practices that can cut down menstruation, or even eliminate it for lengths of time. Some practices work directly on the pituitary gland (sirshasana); others deflect prana from its downward motion to an upward one (maha bandha); others bring one-pointedness of mind and total sublimation of sensual desire (dharana, dhyana, samadhi). However, this only occurs when these practices are performed intensely (for instance, sirshasana held for two – three hours at a time) in combination with a dedicated yogic routine, under the guidance of a guru.

This kind of information prompts some doctors to ask if cessation is always a sign of ill-health; maybe it indicates 'super health'. Yet no periods is not in itself a sign of spiritual development. Often it is a sign of physical or emotional imbalance than can best be rectified by a combination of medical advice and a balanced program of yogic practices.

True spirituality comes with the predominance of *sattwa*, purity and light, on every level of our being. Sattwa on the physical plane involves harmonious and balanced functioning of the body in accordance with the laws of nature.

The *Gita* says: "Yoga is harmony. Not for him who eats too much, nor for him who eats too little; not for him who sleeps too little, or for him who sleeps too much." (6:16) This applies to every aspect of life, including your menstrual cycle. Except in rare cases, this means not elimination of menstruation, but natural, regular and painless menstruation. Yogic practices are beneficial in developing a sattwic body and this promotes a sattwic frame of mind. Through yoga we do not eliminate the body's natural functions, but refine them so that they do not distract the mind.

Overweight

Weight reduction is not the aim of yoga, yet yoga has won a reputation as an effective and permanent way to manage a weight problem. This is not the result of any special diet, nor of hectic exercise. Yoga offers a suitable 'diet' in the original Greek sense: a manner of living. Yoga offers us a harmonious attitude to living, in accord with our needs and nature. Yoga does not focus on fat at all, but on you. Involving you as a person, not just as a body, yoga offers practical techniques that not only give freedom from fat and the prison of constant dieting, but also develops health and harmony in every aspect of your life.

Yoga therapy

The first step then is to make time for an integrated yoga sadhana – from that all the rest will follow.

Asana: Many people feel that to lose weight, they must huff and puff and work themselves into a lather of perspiration. Asanas seem a little too easy. You probably will perspire while practising your asanas at first, but this is not the main point. Medical research shows that asanas reduce the amount of cholesterol and liquid fats in the blood, and in this and other ways, help towards harmonizing the inner body mechanisms. Particularly in women, increased weight may be connected with imbalances in the hormones of the reproductive system. A sluggish thyroid could also be a

154

contributing factor. Asanas not only tone up sagging muscles, they work on the deeper body systems to rectify any hormonal imbalance and massage the internal organs. Weight loss is evenly distributed and the body remoulded.

More importantly, the proper practice of asanas makes us more aware of that inner voice that guides us to maximum health. The body has an intelligence of its own, and we learn through asana practice to pay attention to the many small signs and subtle messages from the body. We learn what to eat, when and how much, when to work harder, when we need rest, and so many other things that help us maintain health and vigour. As you learn through yoga to pay attention to this inner voice, sometimes you will be surprised to find that it is not food at all you want. You might be wanting sleep, a walk, to relax. Food as a substitute would not satisfy your need, and would only increase your weight.

Asanas do not deplete our energy, as do many forms of exercise and sport. Rather they conserve and renew energy that helps to overcome the heaviness and lethargy experienced by women whose weight is excessive. Initially, asana practice should include dynamic practices such as tiryaka tadasana, and surya namaskara, and simple classical postures including vajrasana and pranamasana. Later the duration of your asana practice can be reduced to allow more time for pranayama – particularly bhastrika and nadi shodhana.

Shatkarmas: For more effective weight loss asanas must be supplemented by a proper schedule of kunjal kriya in alternation with shankhaprakshalana. As our weight increases and the longer we maintain extra weight, the more the inner clockwork of the body becomes slow and out of phase. Shatkarmas reinforce the effects of asana, and tone up this sluggish metabolism.

Laghoo shankhaprakshalana brings a rapid drop in blood sugar, encouraging the body to draw on its fat reserves to restore the difference. It also tones up the liver, which is vital to the storage of fats, and their reconversion into useable blood sugar.

155

Kunjal kriya is also helpful, increasing the efficiency of the digestive system and eliminating 'false hunger' due to excess acidity. As fats are dissolved, many unwanted substances stored in the fat cells are thrown into the blood. Both these kriyas speed up the elimination of toxins and bring welcome lightness to the body.

Relaxation: Proper relaxation with yoga nidra or even deeper meditation techniques is an essential part of your program. It is commonly thought that too much tension will make you thin, and that if you are overweight you will only become fatter by relaxing. For women, particularly, this is not always the case. Some people react to tension by reducing their food intake, but the greater number – and most women among them – find themselves eating more, not less, in an effort to compensate. Very often, when we become tired and edgy, what we really want is some time to ourselves, time to relax. Women in particular, in and out of the kitchen all day, often mistake this lack of energy to indicate a need for 'refreshment' – food refreshment. Actually, the food is not needed by the body and becomes fat.

Tension also prevents us from really enjoying food. Because the mind is distracted, we cannot pay full attention to the flavour of food and even after an adequate meal, we feel unsatisfied. To overcome this, we eat more – frequently those fried or sweet goodies that pile on weight.

Moreover, continual tension upsets the body mechanisms, resulting in further weight gain. Relaxation is essential in order to relieve the tensions that distort our relationship to food, and encourage in us a more sensitive appreciation of internal cues. In terms of overall personality development, tension reduction is even more important than weight reduction and points the way to the real purpose of yoga.

Psychological factors

Overweight generally results from overeating rather than other causes such as heredity, hormone deficiencies and so on. Fat people are fat because they eat too much as a matter of habit – a habit with deep emotional roots. Becoming fat is often a reaction to insecurity, sexual frustrations, anxiety and anger. Many people with deep feelings of insecurity experience themselves as consciousness – the 'real me' – locked inside a hollow body. They try to assuage their fears and insecurity by stuffing up this hollow space with food. This makes them feel more solid; the fat gives them a sense of identity, of existing in their own right. On the other hand, a fat woman may feel that her fat is a buffer between herself and a threatening world. Anger and aggression are unacceptable feelings to many, especially women, and they must not be directly expressed. But they create a restlessness inside that keeps us prowling for food. For others, loneliness, loss and pain are blotted out for a moment while eating; food provides an escape, a comfort, a momentary oblivion.

Chronically obese people use food as a narcotic drug, but like any other addict, the food junky feels tremendously guilty and overreacts by dieting or fasting. The compulsive eater feels a split between the 'good' person who starves, and the 'bad' person who stuffs. The pity is that, though she eats to the point of pain, the food addict is so guilty that she does not really taste a single mouthful. She eats a mountain of food but gets no enjoyment, so she is never really satisfied.

Fad diets

Diets do not work simply because they cannot resolve these deep emotional conflicts. The only way to provide the inner nourishment we are searching for in food is to practise yoga, not for weight reduction, but for self discovery.

The compulsive eater is out of touch with real hunger – stomach hunger. She eats from nervousness, anticipation of later hunger, and from 'mouth hunger' ("I don't feel hungry in my stomach, but I *must* have something in my mouth"). Diets further complicate this. You lose touch with the experience of hunger and the ability to satisfy it because you eat according to some artificial standard (e.g. calories) and not according to the body's promptings. The result is that you break the diet and eat everything in sight because you cannot withstand the deprivation.

The constant see-saw of body weight due to alternate dieting and indulgence can also upset the body's energy balance on both physical and pranic levels. This disturbs the nerves, glands and enzymes, and may result in malfunctioning of the brain centre (satiety centre) that tells us to stop eating when we have had enough.

Eat normal food

You did not get fat overnight, and you will not become thin overnight either. Whichever diet you choose must be one that you can live on for several months, and one that re-educates your tastes. Fad diets are deficient in certain elements, and in its efforts to supply these missing necessities, the body's metabolism becomes imbalanced. One-food diets and extremely low calorie diets are only a temporary measure and do not establish permanent, healthy food habits.

A balanced diet of wholefoods, as unprocessed as possible, ensures that the body has all the vital nutrients for health. Unrefined foods (whole grains, vegetables, fruit) are rich in fibre and satisfy the appetite more readily than refined food. Foods high in fibre maintain a healthy digestion, and in contrast to refined foods, supply few or no calories. More importantly, a normal, balanced diet takes the emphasis off 'dieting' – we do not feel deprived – and it establishes a healthy eating pattern to maintain a healthy body weight.

Learn to like simple, unprocessed foods. Eat a little of everything – even the so called 'forbidden fruits' like chocolate, sweets and cake. The key is to eat these a little and not every day. Fix one day a week when you will allow yourself some extra treat to take away the feeling of always being on a diet. (After a short while, these 'extra treats' will be less fascinating as you come to appreciate simpler, more wholesome foods.) It is not the occasional feast that puts on weight, but the day by day overindulgence. On a balanced diet you will find you are eating less and enjoying it more.

Helpful habits to adopt

- Drink plenty of water between meals.
- Start meals with salad or soup. In South India rasam is taken at the end of the meal, but while you are dieting, drink some as a soup before you start.
- Eat plenty of vegetables: they are rich in nutrients and low in calories.
- Avoid extra ghee on idli, rice and chappatis. Reduce fried food and do not eat sweets on a daily basis. Learn to drink juices, tea and coffee with less sugar.
- Do not eat between meals – take only water, tea, coffee or buttermilk at the allotted time *without* tiffin or snacks.
- Eat slowly. From the moment you take your first mouthful to the moment the brain's satiation centre signals 'enough' is at least twenty minutes. Eating quickly, you might eat more in twenty minutes than you need. Eating slowly enables you to savour your food and gives the body time to assess its real needs.
- Sit in vajrasana *before* and *after* meals. Vajrasana after meals aids digestion. Before meals, it gives you time to slow down and become more aware of the act of eating. It gives you time to remember your sankalpa.

Timing is more important

Yogic eating puts more emphasis on the timing of food rather than an exotic diet. Eat your meals at the same time every day. This regularity stabilizes the metabolism. Your body comes to know how much food to expect, and body temperature and activity level automatically adjust to burn up all the food consumed. You will be less inclined to eat between meals, because body rhythms and hunger eventually coincide with meal times. Any gnawing sensations between meals are then more easily recognized as anxiety rather than hunger, soothed by relaxation or yoga nidra rather than a raid on the refrigerator.

Eat early at night. It is the custom in some countries to eat late in the night, 8.00, 9.00 or even 10.00 p.m. Our last meal should be taken three to four hours before sleeping so that digestion is almost complete. We do not need much energy while sleeping, and the food we eat just before going to bed simply goes to fat.

Eating later at night also has other detrimental effects on the body. During sleep the digestive process continues, although at a slower pace. The energy that would otherwise be used for repairing and restoring the body is diverted towards digestion. Our sleep is therefore less efficacious and less satisfactory. We often wake up in the morning feeling dull and sluggish.

On the other hand, although digestion does not stop, it is slowed down and becomes less efficient. When a fire burns well, there is little or no smoke. When we slow it by putting damp wood or blocking the air, far more smoke is produced. So too with the fire of digestion, when digestion is efficient, there are few unwanted by-products. When we slow down digestion in sleep, there is more 'smoke' in the form of unwanted acidity, gas, phlegm and fat. Eating early ensures an efficient digestion and more satisfying sleep. It is easier to get up in the morning and we also wake up feeling fresh and bright.

In our ashrams, the swamis eat at 10.00 a.m. and 5.00 p.m. with something hot to drink at 6.30 a.m. and 1.30 p.m. This enables us to satisfy our food requirements with only two meals a day, without allowing time to get too hungry in between. These timings also coincide with the body rhythms which make maximum use of the food taken at these times. Energy is available when we most need it – during the working day – and the body is light for sadhana in the early morning and the night. If you can adopt these timings, you will find many advantages, and you will find your weight spontaneously balances over time, without heartache. During the changeover period, you might feel like something to eat at your old meal time, especially at night. A hot drink will help to satisfy it. This craving should disappear after ten to fifteen days.

Don't feel guilty

The most important aspect of yogic living is to stop judging what you eat and stop dieting. Instead, *observe* the way you eat and become more aware of what you need. Through awareness and observation, find the amount of food that satisfies you physically and emotionally, and make sure you eat it all – no less, no more. Even if it seems like a lot when all put together, eat what you need at the allotted time. If you overeat at one meal, avoid the guilty temptation to skip the next; this will only throw you further out of balance.

Yoga enables us to experience a positive body awareness, fostering self-acceptance and reliance on your own inner voice. You begin to see yourself as a normal person, and then you eat like a normal person – without guilt. Yoga does not aim to reduce fat, but to reduce spiritual ignorance and all kinds of suffering. The goal of yoga is not to make the body light, but to enlighten the mind. If you keep this before you always, your body will cease to be a burden and will become a blessing.

Practice program

Overweight:
   Asana: Kati chakrasana (20), tiryaka·tadasana (20), surya namaskara (6–12 rounds), shavasana, jhulan lurhakanasana (20), naukasanchalana (10), chakki chalanasana (10 each side), supta vajrasana or ushtrasana (minimum 7 breaths), marjariasana (10 breaths), pranamasana (30–50 breaths), vajrasana (before meals five minutes, after meals ten minutes).
   Pranayama: Bhastrika pranayama (3–5) rounds.
   Other: Yoga nidra (30 minutes any time in the day).
   Shatkarma: Laghoo shankhaprakshalana (weekly for three months), kunjal kriya (twice weekly for one month then once a week).
   Diet: Meals at 10.00 a.m. and 5.00–6.00 p.m.

161

Pregnancy

The eternal mother, big with child is the archetypal image of fertility, abundance and productivity, and the state of pregnancy is the primary symbol of creative consciousness and optimism. Although such a commonplace, pregnancy is a total experience, a special condition, a forceful example of the intimate connection between body and mind. It is a time when it is extremely important that the various dimensions of a woman's being are in harmony. The practices of yoga promote optimum health of body and mind, unifying a mother's physical, emotional and spiritual growth with that of her child.

Contemplating conception

The regular practice of yoga before conception is the ideal preparation for pregnancy. The mother-to-be will have gained flexibility and suppleness from the practice of asanas, Pranayama ensures that she is charged with vitality enough for two, and meditation promotes the serenity which is traditionally associated with approaching motherhood.

More importantly, the practice of yoga by both parents will enable them to develop as fitting hosts for a child of more than ordinary spiritual capacity. It is possible for a child to be born with partial or total awakening of kundalini. Such individuals are spiritually developed from birth itself and are able to make great contributions to humanity.

Such children are rare, and rare also the dedicated parents who are able to bring them into the world, yet we should never forget that the possibility is there. The spiritual preparedness of the parents is an overwhelming factor in the conception of every child, whose consciousness will be moulded and fed by the spiritual essence of the parents.

Preparatory practices

Yoga can be of great value during pregnancy, even for beginners, who will find most of the practices well within their capacity. For successful pregnancy and delivery emphasis should be placed on the development of the following areas:

Stomach muscles: Strength in the abdominal region will ensure that the baby is carried well, assisting proper development. During delivery these muscles are most important in pushing the child from the womb. The most important asanas for this area are supta vajrasana, shashankasana, ushtrasana, hamsasana, matsyasana and the shakti bandha series.

Spine: A strong, healthy spine is necessary for the proper functioning of the nervous system and general flexibility. A strong spine will prevent the drooping shoulders often developed during pregnancy because of the extra weight being carried. The practices most recommended for the spine are supta vajrasana, marjariasana, vyaghrasana, ardha matsyendrasana, paschimottanasana, bhujangasana and surya namaskara.

Back muscles: The extra weight of the child will also put a great strain on the back muscles, and added strength in this area is a great advantage. Bhujangasana, paschimottanasana, halasana, sarvangasana, shashankasana and supta vajrasana are very beneficial.

Pelvis: A relaxed, flexible pelvic area makes for easy childbirth. Marjariasana, shashankasana, vyaghrasana, matsyasana, all squatting poses, siddha yoni asana and other crossed legged poses are most useful in this respect.

163

Asanas throughout pregnancy

During the first three months of pregnancy, the program of preparatory asanas may be continued as usual, but some adjustment will be required after this time.

The beginning of the fourth month marks the time to stop asanas involving strenuous upward stretching or violent stomach contractions. Sirshasana and sarvangasana are usually discontinued at this time, but they may be replaced by pranamasana and jalandhara bandha respectively.

From the sixth month both forward bending asanas (like paschimottanasana) and extreme backward bending asanas (ushtrasana) become increasingly difficult. Supta vajrasana and squatting asanas are to be avoided from this time if there is any tendency to premature delivery or to prolapse.

The pawanmuktasana series is used at this time, where the muscles and joints are all thoroughly exercised in a way that ensures maximum flexibility and optimum blood circulation, with a minimum of energy expenditure. Squatting postures should still be practised for loosening the hips and toning the pelvic floor. Kali asana is a simple squatting position used in natural childbirth. In order to practise this asana during delivery, a woman must be able to squat with both heels flat on the ground for ten to fifteen minutes and be able to rise smoothly and easily once the child's head has emerged. There are numerous physical and emotional advantages to using kali asana for delivery and various squatting asanas provide ideal preparation. They include crow walking, chopping wood and namaskarasana, and may be continued throughout pregnancy along with marjariasana, kandharasana and pranamasana.

Sitting in cross-legged asanas such as sukhasana, swastikasana, ardha padmasana, padmasana or siddha yoni asana is recommended throughout. These avoid circulation problems in the legs and swelling of the ankles that frequently develops in later pregnancy and after sitting for long periods of time in chairs. In the final months sitting cross legged helps to reduce the natural sensation of body heaviness.

164

Pranayama

The various pranayamas are most important during pregnancy, ensuring efficient removal of waste products and plentiful supply of oxygen for both mother and child. Pranayama purifies and calms the nervous system to induce a feeling of pleasant wellbeing.

Shastra tells us that during the first three months the developing child has no pranic supply of its own. During this time the baby is completely dependent on the prana of its mother. It is therefore extremely important that you practise plenty of pranayama during the early months of your pregnancy.

A suitable program would include deep yogic breathing, sheetali and sheetkari, kapalbhati, bhastrika and nadi shodhana. If possible, these practices should be repeated in the evening.

At the end of the third month, the panchapranas begin to operate in the child's body, and he is therefore endowed with his own pranic resources. Nevertheless, the mother should continue her pranayama to ensure abundant energy for them both, as a means of maintaining lightness in her own body and mind, and as preparation for delivery room.

Around mid-term, the growth of the baby enlarges the uterus to such an extent that the diaphragm is pushed upwards, resulting in a sensation of shortness of breath. At this time, continuation of deep yogic breathing is helpful. Kapalbhati may be stopped and samavritti pranayama with its short ratios, may be introduced. Bhastrika may become difficult around this time, but should be continued even if in modified form. Nadi shodhana is the easiest and most satisfactory pranayama for this time.

Some special problems

Morning sickness: During the early part of pregnancy most women experience a strong feeling of nausea, perhaps with actual vomiting, usually in the mornings. Together with this discomfort comes dullness and lethargy, and a loss of appetite that may develop into an aversion to particular foods and cooking odours. Morning sickness may occasionally last for several months, but most women are heartened to know that it generally stops spontaneously towards the end of the third month.

In the meantime, the intensity of this problem can be reduced with attention to diet and the practice of kunjal kriya. Avoid oily and heavy food at all times, especially at night, and try to eat the night meal between 5.00 p.m. and 7.00 p.m. In the morning rather than suffer unnecessarily for some hours, practise kunjal kriya (stomach washing with salt water). Kunjal cleans the stomach and puts a stop to nausea. It stimulates the appetite and digestive fire. You will feel fresh and clear mentally, and there will be abundant energy and optimism to begin the day. Since vomiting frequently occurs spontaneously during early pregnancy, this conscious vomiting cannot be regarded as harmful, especially if you remain relaxed and don't strain.

Constipation: As the baby grows heavier and changes position in later pregnancy, many women develop constipation, which is not only discomforting in its own right, but increases backache and lethargy. Adequate roughage in the diet and drinking plenty of water will help, but not completely eliminate this problem, for which laghoo shankhaprakshalana is recommended.

The shatkarma practice of laghoo shankhaprakshalana is a method of cleansing the entire digestive system with emphasis on clearing the bowels. It is practised by taking six glasses of salt water, interspersed with asanas. This practice does not involve stomach contractions and the asanas recommended are all safe and possible to perform even in later pregnancy.

Laghoo shankhaprakshalana will definitely eliminate constipation, creating a feeling of ease and lightness in the body. It should be practised once or twice a week after the sixth month. Where the mother shows a tendency to water retention, this may be minimized by drinking a large glass of

166

barley water, coconut water or rice kunji as the first meal after the practice, and if necessary taking a saltless lunch.

Oedema: The retention of excess water in the body; and shows as a swelling of the face, hands, ankles, wrists or feet. This swelling tends to increase towards the end of the day. Some oedema in pregnancy is normal, especially in the later months, but it may be minimized by the practice of pawanmuktasana. The first series of pawanmuktasana (anti-rheumatic) is to be practised in the late afternoon or early evening, with special attention to the asanas for feet and legs. This will help squeeze water from the tissue spaces in the body, improving blood circulation and the transportation of fluid through the circulatory and lymph systems. Kandharasana, or the simple form of matsyasana, will also stimulate the kidneys to remove excess fluid from the body.

Too much salt is to be avoided, but too drastic reduction of salt is also harmful – it may lead to muscle cramp and interfere with milk production. It is better, instead, to take natural diuretics like tender coconut water, barley water or rice kunji.

Toxaemia: While some water retention is normal, when there is a sudden increase in oedema after the fifth month, it could be a warning of toxaemia. Metabolic toxaemia of pregnancy (MTP) is a serious condition that can occur late in pregnancy, affecting 7–12% of women carrying their first babies and 5–6% of women bearing later children. In addition to excessive oedema, other symptoms include high blood pressure and protein in the urine. There may also be severe headache, blurred vision and abdominal pain. Toxaemia rarely develops to the final stage (which may be fatal) if a woman is under regular medical supervision, and for this reason, if no other, periodic medical check-ups are advisable throughout pregnancy.

Toxaemia is primarily a problem of poor nutrition, especially lack of protein and B-vitamins. It not only affects women in poor countries where food is scarce, but also women in developed countries who eat too much refined, instant food to the neglect of grains, fruit and vegetables. Toxaemia may be systematically avoided by a balanced yogic diet, which will include vegetables of all kinds, some fruit, some milk or curd, and plenty of whole grains – wheat, unpolished rice, barley (jowar), millet (ragi), corn (makai).

Spiritual nourishment

In early pregnancy, the developing embryo is still just a cluster of new cells in the womb, without any individual existence apart from the mother. With the inspiration of the panchapranas in the third month, the developing baby is endowed with its own source of vital energy and attains a physical individuality. In the fourth month the *jiva* enters the physical vehicle being prepared for it, and from this time the unborn child has its own awareness, its own atman. From this moment, a mother is carrying an individual with his own unique spiritual endowments and spiritual potential. The mother then has to nourish the child not only physically, but also spiritually through sharing the purity and power of her own consciousness.

The wise have always seen that the basic fabric of a child's spiritual personality is woven in the womb, and this knowledge has been passed down to us through the shastras, in stories like those of Prahlad and Parikshit.

The father of Prahlad, Hiranyakashipu, was a demonic dictator, a tyrant who suppressed all the natural freedoms of his people, especially their freedom to worship. While carrying Prahlad, his mother left the court of her evil husband and passed her confinement in the ashram of the sage Narada who instructed her in the spiritual truths and in the special glories of Lord Vishnu. Prahlad, though still in the womb, also shared in this initiation, and even in the face of his father's fury, he was a staunch devotee of Lord Vishnu from early childhood. Prahlad's devotion to Sri Hari endowed him with such inner strength that he became instrumental in the overthrow of his father's tyranny and later attained the highest realization.

The life of Parikshit was also guided by experience in the womb. After the war of Kurukshetra, Aswathamma sent a missile to wipe out the entire Pandava progeny – born and unborn – particularly aimed at Uttara who had conceived Arjuna's grandson.

In fulfilment of his promise to Kunti, Sri Krishna took the form of a point of light and entered the womb of Uttara. The baby in the womb who had felt a great heat approach, suddenly felt cool. He saw a light revolving around him, protecting him from the scorching missile. This child grew up to be a righteous king, well loved by all, and he became the instrument for the transmission of the *Srimad Bhagavatam*. He was called Parikshit – one who searches – for throughout his life he was searching for the light which had protected him before his birth, the light that he ultimately came to know as Sri Krishna, personification of love and light.

Tales such as these are age old reminders of the importance of blessing and gracing our children even before they enter the world. Today paediatricians and psychiatrists are also of the opinion that some qualities of personality may result from the specific environment of the child before birth. The chemical aspects of the uterine environment, particularly the correct proportions of all the necessary hormones are dependent on the health and emotional welfare of the mother. It is not now possible – and it may never be – to distinguish the effects of the pre birth experience from natural genetic inheritance. However, it is a matter of fact that the health and mental attitudes of the mother are reflected in the development of the child. Illness and nervous tension in their mothers definitely have an adverse effect on babies, before as well as after birth.

In this regard, yogic relaxation and meditation practices are most important. Because of the many subtle changes in the body, pregnancy can be a time of emotional vulnerability for many women, with cravings for strange foods, intense dreams, sudden depressions or tears without reason. Such feelings are not only exhausting but they can be of such

169

intensity that they further disturb the harmony of the body. There are many yogic relaxation techniques that can be used to minimize emotional stress and to create a harmonious environment for the coming child.

The child in the womb is protected from, but not impervious to the outside world, and is particularly sensitive to sound. The baby's heart beat will jump at an unexpected and loud noise, and will register the ringing of bells or the singing of lullabies. One of the most constant and dominant factors in the baby's uterine environment is the reassuring rhythm of the mother's heartbeat.

When a mother practises mantra japa (repetition of a mantra) she is adding another dimension to the baby's sensitivity to sound – a spiritual dimension that will evoke a resonance at the very core of the child's consciousness. Mantra japa and dhyana allow a woman to enter the depths of her being where her consciousness merges with, and may exert a positive influence on, the consciousness of the growing child.

Yoga nidra

Yoga nidra is one of the most flexible meditation techniques in yoga, in that it can be practised virtually any time of day, and varied in duration from twenty minutes to one hour. It is practised lying down rather than in a classical sitting asana. These characteristics are very advantageous for practice during pregnancy.

Yoga nidra is generally practised in shavasana (lying on the back) but many women find this makes them short of breath, especially later in pregnancy. In this case, matsya-kridasana is recommended as an alternative. In this asana you lie on one side with one leg straight, while the other (upper) knee is bent and supported on a cushion so that there is no pressure on the abdomen. This is a favourite position of doctors for delivery, and a pose which many people spontaneously adopt for sleeping – a very comfortable alternative for expectant mothers.

170

At a time when women are especially sensitive to their bodies, this technique uses relaxed awareness of the body to induce relaxation of the mind. Once this is established, a series of symbols and images is evoked, to be viewed with the detached awareness of a witness. This awareness is vital to yogic growth and as it increases in power and scope, positive emotions of love, peace and harmony will permeate your life. These provide the ideal emotional climate for the baby's development and are the perfect protection once the child is delivered from the womb. This attitude of witnessing is also important during childbirth, for it breaks the mother's identification with her bodily pain and helps her to be more fully conscious of the events taking place.

The visualization sequences in yoga nidra are especially useful in facilitating the mother's subtle perception of the growth of the child in her womb. In the supersensitive and expansive state of yoga nidra, the mother is not only more in touch with herself, but also with her child. Conscious realization of the communion transforms the time of pregnancy into an opportunity for the mother's spiritual growth and rebirth.

Life in the womb

Medical science has discovered a good deal about the day-to-day development of the human embryo, its growth into a foetus and its ultimate birth as a child. At about six or seven days after conception the new organism embeds itself in the lining of the uterus. At this stage it is called an embryo until its species is recognizable, which in human beings is about the seventh week. After that the organism is called a foetus until the time of its birth.

The limbs appear as tiny buds on the embryo when it is less than a month old. At that time, the embryo is completely formed, although it is less than half an inch in length. The heart is usually beating a few days before the end of the first month of life. At this time the baby is enclosed in a sort of bag called the amniotic sac, in a completely liquid environment. He will remain in the sac until it breaks at birth, or a little before, exposing the child to air.

By the seventh week, the embryo is recognizably human. The brain has formed sufficiently to send out electrical impulses and even at this early stage the brain is the co-ordinator of the other organs. Growth is very rapid. The embryo grows at the rate of about a millimetre a day. This is not regular growth, but the development of first one portion and then another of what will be the human body. The skeleton begins to develop when the embryo is forty-six to forty-eight days old.

The foetus can move and be quite active during the third month and certainly is so from that time on. It develops muscles, can move its limbs and soon learns to grasp. The muscular contractions which will later become facial exp-ressions can be recorded. In most cases, the mother does not feel the movement of her child until he has grown sufficiently that the uterus has expanded above the natural container of the pelvis, usually the fourth or fifth month.

The nervous system is also developing – the foetus can react to pressure and loud noise. This sensitivity to outside stimulus is perhaps the most important thing about the foetus. The influence of the pre birth environment is extremely important in determining what the individual reactions will be. We do not know as much as we might about the nature of the prenatal environment and its influence on the physical and mental health of the eventual adult. We do know that X-rays, many drugs – including nicotine – and other substances have some adverse influence on the formation and growth of the foetus.

It is believed that the first part of the human body to become sensitive is the mouth. Only later do the eyes, hands and other body parts achieve sufficient nerve endings to be sensitive to touch. By the end of the ninth week of foetal life the only important parts of the body which are not sensitive to touch are the back and the top of the head, which will remain insensitive until after birth.

172

By the end of the fourth month of life, the baby has gained half the height he will reach before birth. Certainly during the fifth month his movements can be detected by the mother. He sleeps and wakes, and has already acquired some of his favourite physical positions. During the sixth month, the child begins to accumulate some fat and he gets the buds for his permanent teeth behind the milk teeth that are now developing. By the end of the sixth month the child is as much as a foot long and weighs about half a kilo. Fingernails have started to grow and he is very active.

The last three months of life in the womb see the completion of many body parts, but this is mostly just polishing off. During this final period the child is primarily growing, gaining weight and achieving muscular control. By the time he is ready to be born he is so big that his movements are extremely hampered by the restricted area now provided by the uterus. His demands are such that the placenta is no longer able to fulfil them all.

This spectacular growth occurs in the mother's own body with no conscious effort on her part. With the help of various yoga practices, however, the expectant mother can become more aware of the foetus in the womb, fully experiencing this most intimate of relationships.

Childbirth

Birth begins when a birth hormone (pitocin) is secreted by the pituitary gland, and the amniotic sac breaks, releasing the fluid that has protected the child from shocks and traumas. The occasional contractions of the uterus that are felt throughout pregnancy increase in frequency and intensity, and the 'labour' pains have begun.

First stage of labour: These contractions last 15 seconds to one minute, beginning with a gradual tightening of the womb that comes to a strong peak, then slowly subsides. This stage may last 2–24 hours, depending on the size and position of the baby, the size of the mother's pelvic area, and the behaviour of the uterus. At this time the lengthwise muscles of the uterus are involuntarily working to pull open the circular muscles of the cervix. As the cervix opens wider (effacement) the contractions become stronger and more frequent until the cervix is fully dilated.

Transition: That phase of labour just before the cervix opens to a full 10 centimetres to accommodate the baby's head and allow the baby to enter the birth canal. This phase is the one that is usually felt to be most painful, and may be accompanied by nausea, leg cramps, trembling, backache and increasing irritability and fear.

Second stage labour: This begins with a strong desire to bear down and push the baby out. However, this urge must be restrained until the cervix is fully opened. Once this is achieved, you may fully surrender to the desire to push. Here the pain of transition is transformed into a feeling of high exhilaration as you take an active part in the baby's journey into the world.

It is in this stage that anaesthetic is usually given, but given the proper training and preparation, this may be avoided. A 'natural childbirth' will leave you alert at the climax of birth, which is experienced not as pain but as joy.

Third stage of labour: The delivery of the placenta (umbilical cord) which is expelled after the baby is born. This usually takes place within 5–10 minutes, and with this clear removal of the 'afterbirth' the birth of the child is fully accomplished.

Yoga in childbirth

Childbearing is not a disease that should need routine drugs, anaesthetics, or other medications. Although there are times when help is needed, most deliveries are normal and can be carried out free from distress. Nor is childbirth bound to be an excruciatingly painful experience – it becomes painful only through our own fears and inadequate preparations. We must distinguish here between pain and natural, strenuous exertion which may be demanding, but also exhilarating.

Through the use of yogic techniques, for some women childbirth is totally pain free. While most women experience half an hour or so of pain or great discomfort at the end of the first stage of labour, yogic methods can definitely minimize this discomfort, even if it is not eliminated absolutely. More importantly, yoga enables us to remain fully *aware* during the delivery, responding spontaneously to the innate wisdom of the body profoundly manifest at this time. When she has been practising yoga regularly, a woman will be able to translate her experience into a practical method of painless, *conscious* birthing.

Kali asana: The squatting pose adopted for delivery by women in traditional cultures. It is the most effective posture for the later stages of labour and delivery. For several decades, modern women have usually given birth lying on the back with the legs raised and knees apart. This is especially true of sedated, hospital births where the mother's ankles are usually supported in braces above the delivery table. In this position, the birth canal faces horizontally and upwards, requiring women to labour against gravity. This requires considerably more muscular effort than a squatting pose, and further energy is misdirected, going to waste in the back and leg muscles.

In Kali asana the birth canal and pelvic floor face downward, taking advantage of gravity and apana shakti, the downward flowing energy of the pelvis. This squatting position enables a woman to bear down with great efficiency, force and control, with every contraction of the uterus. Labour is completed more quickly. With adequate yogic preparation, a woman can deliver easily from Kali asana, requiring only nominal guidance and assistance from the attendant doctor or midwife.

Kali asana enhances the mother's physical and spiritual participation in the birth. She partakes of the confidence and strength of goddess Kali, and the birth becomes a powerful self-expression, a ritual of attainment through right exertion.

175

In most delivery wards, women are encouraged to deliver on their backs because this position makes it easier for the doctor or midwife to assist the birth. Thus although kali asana is very effective for delivery, ultimately it is best to decide on the position of birthing in conjunction with your doctor/midwife rather than insisting on kali asana if they are not agreeable to it.

Pranayama: In this regard, primary emphasis in the delivery room is placed on pranayama. As pregnancy progresses, we emphasize the relaxing and invigorating aspect of pranayama, learning to harmonize the breath with the feeling and movements of the body to clarify the mind. At the actual time of birth this harmonization of breath, body and mind enables a woman to link the rhythm of the breath with the contractions of the uterus, allowing her to control the labour and maintain an exhilarating awareness throughout. Rhythmic breathing also helps to minimize fatigue and to avoid fear and pain.

You might think that pranayama will be thrown to the winds in the drama of giving birth, especially if the baby is your first. Definitely it helps if your husband, friend or some trained person is there to hold your hand and guide you with instructions for breathing and relaxing. However, these techniques may also be rehearsed during daily pranayama practice and visualized in yoga nidra, so that you slip into them automatically at this time.

There are four types of breathing used during delivery:
1. Deep yogic breathing at the beginning of contraction
2. Bhastrika as the contraction peaks
3. Normal breathing between contractions
4. Antar kumbhaka (inner retention) while pushing in late second stage

As the labour begins, tune into your breath with deep yogic breathing, reflected in the rising and falling of the navel. Then, as the contraction begins to tighten, start bhastrika pranayama (rapid panting). Here, however, we make a modification to classical bhastrika and, rather than breathing through the nostrils, we practise panting through the open mouth. As the contraction passes, allow the breath to flow in naturally – a long smooth inhalation – and use the outgoing breath to take out the tightness from the body on exhalation. Then allow the natural breath to flow without control, but with awareness on the feeling at the navel. With the first stirrings of the next contraction, deepen the breathing until the full yogic breath is established then repeat the cycle. This pattern of breathing continues into transition where one must temporarily resist the urge to bear down and push prematurely. This can be controlled by transferring awareness from the navel to the centre of the chest, and focusing the mind on the feeling of lightness induced by bhastrika.

In second stage labour you will find the panting breath almost continuous. This is the time to assist the baby by surrendering to the desire for pushing, and this is best facilitated by holding the breath while you exert maximum force. A rapid deep expulsion of breath will follow, and bhastrika will be spontaneously resumed.

Throughout delivery it is important to relax completely between contractions, with special emphasis on relaxing the muscles of the pelvic floor and perineum. Clear, precise location and control of these muscles will have become easy if you have been practising moola bandha during pregnancy, and by using the rapid rotation from yoga nidra the whole body will relax readily. If the mother is sufficiently strong and healthy, she has much to gain from giving birth without the use of anaesthetic. The drugged deliveries that have become standard unfortunately exclude the mother from conscious involvement in the birth, depriving her of the opportunity for a fresh spiritual awakening.

After delivery
During pregnancy the body is undergoing constant change, and this continues after the delivery for some time – but in reverse. Within a few hours of the birth the body will begin

to return to its normal condition. Mild contractions of the uterus will be felt as the womb begins to return to its normal shape and size. At the birth, the uterus usually weighs about one kilo, but within two weeks it shrinks back to around 350 grams. Breast feeding has a positive effect by stimulating these contractions which are sometimes called 'after pains' although they are rarely painful.

For about ten weeks after the birth there will be a continuous discharge from the womb, called lochia, and within six to ten weeks normal menstruation begins again if you are not breast feeding. Mothers who breast feed their children will usually have first ovulation around the twentieth week (fifth month) after the birth, and normal menstruation will return around the twenty-fourth week (six months).

For a day or two after the birth the mother may experience some constipation or urinary difficulty – there might be some hindrance in urinating or even involuntary urination while coughing or laughing. This is due to the stretching and slackness of muscles in the pelvic floor, and is more rapidly overcome where the mother begins to take short walks and to resume some mild yoga practice.

Postnatal depression

For the first few days after the birth, the breasts produce a substance called colostrum. Then, around the third or fourth day there are hormonal changes which cause the milk to flow. As a result of these hormonal changes, every mother finds she feels very low emotionally for a few days. She will usually weep, she might have nightmares, she feels anxious that she is not really mature enough for motherhood, or even that she does not want the baby after all. These feelings usually last only for a few days, but for some women this depression persists for weeks or even months.

Postpartum depression is usually attributed to hormonal imbalance after delivery, and in such cases it is alleviated or overcome by a regular practice of asanas and meditation. However, even mothers who adopt their children may suffer

178

from this problem, which would suggest that the main cause is a woman's insecurity and feelings of inadequacy. Women who suffer in this way frequently doubt their ability to be competent, loving mothers.

Having someone to talk to, someone who can share her feelings is a great help to a woman at this time, and where a woman receives help and reassurance from her family, friends and other mothers, recovery is more rapid. Since negative feelings are exaggerated by fatigue, meditation should be practised to compensate for lack of sleep, and to allow the mother to face her fears rather than suppress them. Some time put aside every day for meditation will help a woman to find that oasis of peace within herself, that place where she is always strong and naturally loving. This daily affirmation will provide her with the ultimate reassurance to help overcome her fears.

Resume yoga soon

Women who have been practising yoga regularly find that their recuperation after delivery is surprisingly rapid, and their susceptibility to the 'baby blues' is minimized. Within a day or two after delivery, yogic breathing and nadi shodhana pranayama can be recommenced, even in bed. If there are no complications, the antirheumatic series of pawanmuktasana can also be resumed. Moola bandha is also valuable at this time to re-establish muscle tone in the pelvic floor.

Most of the changes taking place in a woman's body take place within the first two weeks of delivery, and after two weeks the new mother can safely resume all the asanas she had practised before pregnancy. This should be gradual in the beginning, commencing with the second (anti-gastric) series of pawanmuktasanas then the shakti bandha asanas, later resuming the classical asanas at the rate of one or two a week. Moola bandha and uddiyana bandha should be practised daily to tighten the abdominal muscles and restore the tone of the reproductive organs.

A time to listen

During her pregnancy and in the first few months with the baby, a new mother has so much to gain from the support of other women who are already mothers. This is a time when grandmothers and other 'elders' come into their own, to share their accumulated experience and wisdom. In every culture there are traditions and rituals of childbearing, and we should not be too hasty to dismiss these as superstitions.

In India, for instance, it is the custom for a woman to return to her mother's home during the last three months of pregnancy and to remain there for at least six weeks after the birth. This might seem like an unnecessary fuss but the custom continues to this day because it brings so many benefits. In her mother's house, the expectant mother is freed from the daily routine of housekeeping and is therefore free to take the extra rest she requires in late pregnancy. She has the care and guidance of all the other women of the house who make sure that she follows a proper diet, and instruct her in the use of the various herbal preparations (kashaya and lehas) that are used in India for the health of both mother and child. In this supportive atmosphere, away from the normal demands of running a home, the new mother has time for contemplation and meditation for her own well being and the spiritual nourishment of the child.

After delivery there are further time-tested practices to help a mother regain her balance, physically and emotionally. There is a routine of massage, baths and herbal supplements for both mother and child. These early weeks in her maternal home allow the new mother to learn all the routines of caring for her baby, while providing her with the opportunity to get to know her child. Before she resumes her full responsibilities in her own household, even the most timid has confidence in herself as a mother, and fears and doubts give way to a real pleasure in being with the child.

The customs of India have their counter parts in every society. This information is the heritage of grandmothers and great-grandmothers who depended on such knowledge in the days before hospital deliveries were common, and it is up to today's women to claim this heritage as their own before the old wisdom dies out. While it might not be possible to follow all the old advice in detail, we can gather and preserve its essence.

For instance, it is a custom in India that after the bath, a tiny coal fire is lit and sprinkled with a mixture of herbs and spices (samrani) to give an aromatic smoke. The new mother stands astride this fire to dry her hair, which is further purified by the smoke, and at the same time the warm air from the coals rises up and causes the uterus to contract, so that it soon regains its proper shape and size. In place of this custom we can achieve the same effect by the regular practise of moola bandha, commencing a few days after delivery. The original customs may be cumbersome today, but the essence is sound. If we look carefully, we will find that the essentials of the old customs are to be found in refined form in the practices of yoga, which will meet not only the physical needs of pregnancy, but also spiritual ones.

An initiation
Every time a woman gives birth with the help of yoga, she unites all the resources of her body, mind and soul in a total involvement with the primary forces of life.and consciousness, both of which are individual and universal. Birth is the primary initiation for the child, and provides a chance for spiritual renewal for the mother, for the natural heightening of one's faculties during such an event opens the doors to cosmic communion.

After the pain, so intense it was no pain, with my new born son on my breast, there came the peace – I floated on a still, clear lake of deep blue peace. And like the velvet, silent night descending gently all around, there came an understanding of the pain and the purpose, and I knew why it is we are born. My life has been blessed ever since.

Practice program

Pregnancy:

First 3 months: Continue the sadhana you have been doing
so far. If you are just now beginning, practise the
sadhana 'for beginners' given at the end of this book.
In either case, add the following practices:
Pranayama: Sahaja pranayama (54 rounds), simple
bhastrika pranayama (5 rounds/rest/5 rounds).
Shatkarma: Kunjal kriya (minimum twice weekly).

Beginning the fourth month: Stop your previous sadhana and
commence the following practices:
Asana: Shavasana, titali asana (100), namaskarasana (10),
chakki chalanasana (10 each side), kandharasana
(hold as long as possible), marjariasana (15), kandha
chakrasana (10 each side sitting in sukhasana or
siddha yoni asana), greeva sanchalana (10).
Pranayama: Bhastrika pranayama (7 rounds), nadi
shodhana (10 rounds/rest/10 rounds, ratio 1:1:2).
Shatkarma: Laghoo shankhaprakshalana   (once or
twice weekly).
Other: Yoga nidra (before lunch or at midday),
mantra japa (morning and evening), matsyakridasana
(for sleeping and relaxation).

After delivery: Commence the following:
Asana: Pawanmuktasana part I (10 each side).
Pranayama: Sahaja pranayama (54 rounds), nadi
shodhana pranayama (10 rounds, ratio 1:1:2).
Bandha: Moola bandha (simple, 100 times), moola
bandha (with breath, 10 times).
Other: Yoga nidra.

Later: Practise as follows:
Asana: Pawanmuktasana part II (5 times each increasing
to 10), chakki chalanasana (10 each side).
Bandha: Uddiyana bandha (5 rounds), moola bandha
(simple form, 100 times), moola bandha (with breath,
10 times).
Other: Yoga nidra.

Prolapse

Prolapse is the displacement of, or falling out of position of one of the organs of the body. The bladder may drop, or the rectum, but it is more common for women to find that the uterus has dropped from its correct position.

The uterus, like other organs of the pelvic region, is held in position by a network of muscles and ligaments connected to the centre of the pelvic floor between the anus and vagina (perineum). If these muscles and ligaments tear or stretch, or lose their tone, they become too weak to support the uterus which, under the influence of gravity, sags into the vagina. In severe cases the uterus may actually protrude outside the body.

Symptoms

Uterine prolapse is accompanied by a continuous dull ache in the lower back and, usually, vaginal discharge. Urination is affected due to pressure on the bladder. You may urinate more frequently, perhaps with difficulty. You might also lose control of the bladder so that you pass a little urine when you laugh or cough. Constipation may develop if the uterus presses through the vagina towards the rectum. In severe cases there is often a discomforting feeling that something is coming out of the vagina. The most distinctive individual symptom is that when you lie down on your back and the pull of gravity is relieved, all the other symptoms disappear.

Cause

The major factor in weakening or destroying the supports of the uterus is the stress and strain of childbirth. Of those women with prolapsed wombs, 99% have had at least one baby. Chronic constipation or frequent diarrhoea may also impose excessive strain leading to uterine prolapse, but this is less common. Ageing and heavy physical work also contribute, and the symptoms often appear only after menopause, when the affected muscles may lose tone and ligaments atrophy.

Correction

Once a ligament is torn, it is difficult to reconstitute it without surgery, and extremely weak muscles will need persistent daily exercise over several months before they regain their full strength. Nevertheless, even in cases of severe prolapse, yoga therapy can be beneficial and may eliminate the need for surgery. Definitely mild or recent prolapse can be completely corrected within a few months, with the help of appropriate yoga practices.

The most important practice for this purpose is *vipareeta karani asana*, often called the half shoulder stand. This asana inverts the body at such an angle that not only is the downward drag of gravity relieved, but the uterus falls exactly into its correct position in the pelvic cavity. For therapeutic purposes, this asana must be practised for several minutes at a time, three times a day. Initially you may practise this asana with the help of cushions under the lower back and hips, resting the legs against the wall. With a little regular practice, the pillows can soon be removed and, ultimately, the asana can be maintained without the help of the wall. Once you are steady in the asana, hold it for five minutes at a stretch. If this is not possible, hold the asana as long as you are comfortable, rest for some time in shavasana, then resume the asana for some time.

Another important practice for a strong uterus is *naukasana*, the boat pose. During naukasana there is an automatic inward contraction which lifts the uterus into its correction position and holds it there for some time. The supporting ligaments gradually become stronger.

The practice of naukasana also develops the capacity for moola bandha, the contraction of the cervix and surrounding area. Once vipareeta karani asana is mastered, moola bandha is practised while maintaining the posture. While sitting, both the simple form of moola bandha (rapid contractions) and the complete form (prolonged contraction with kumbhaka) are to be practised for effective therapy and the stimulation of prana – the healing energy naturally present in the body.

At least once a day, time should also be made to practise other mudras and bandhas that will not only restore muscle tone, but also restore the vitality so often depleted by prolapse. Uddiyana bandha, standing or sitting, automatically induces a tight moola bandha. These two are united with jalandhara bandha on the exhaled breath to constitute maha bandha, which should be practised nine times daily. One hundred rapid contractions of ashwini mudra should follow.

Sirshasana, sarvangasana and halasana are also helpful, but any asana which exerts a strong downward pressure on the lower abdomen must definitely be avoided. Asanas to avoid include crow walking, utthanasana, chopping wood, namaskarasana and supta vajrasana. Uttanpadasana, with both legs stretched in front of the body is a useful asana for casual sitting during the day, for it helps exert a slight upward pull on the pelvic organs.

Opening a window

The correction of prolapse through yoga requires persistent and careful practise over several months, maybe even longer if structural damage is severe. However, it must be remembered that no yogic practice is for the body only, and you will experience for yourself the positive effects of your sadhana for your emotional and spiritual wellbeing. The irritation and depression that so often accompany prolapse

185

will give way to a new serenity and emotional stability, and the enhancement of pranic vitality will give fresh enthusiasm not only for yoga, but for the joy of living in general. It is not unusual for women to find that practices initially undertaken for therapy have opened a window on a new dimension of wellbeing that gives a new meaning to life.

Practice program

Prolapse:
Morning: To be practised in the following order:
Uddiyana bandha with moola bandha (standing, 9 rounds, hold as long as possible each time), shavasana, naukasana (5 times, hold as long as possible), moola bandha (sitting, simple, 100 rounds then practise with breath, 11 rounds), vipareeta karani asana (start with 1 minute, increase to 5 minutes), shavasana (in between if necessary).
Before lunch: Vipareeta karani asana (up to 5 minutes).
Evening: Repeat morning program.

Urinary System Disorders

Nearly every woman will suffer from some kind of urinary system disorder at least once during her childbearing years. The most common of these disorders are incontinence and bladder inflammation.

Incontinence

Inability to restrain the flow of urine is called incontinence, whether partial or total. Total loss of control is less common, occurring in the very old or where there has been damage to the nervous system. Partial incontinence occurs more in women after menopause, but it can be present at any age. This manifests in two ways:

1. *Urgency incontinence*: There is a very short time between feeling a desire to urinate and feeling that one must urinate immediately and can no longer hold on.
2. *Stress incontinence*: Small amounts of urine are lost when a woman laughs, coughs or strains. This happens even if the bladder is practically empty.

Causes

There can be several causes for this weakness, including impairment of the nerves due to injury, congenital defects, bladder disorders, and chronic emotional tension. The main cause is weakness of the muscle at the opening of the bladder. During childbirth the muscles of the lower pelvis are stretched and become slack, or they may even be damaged by surgery. Unless conscious efforts are made to compensate for this, these muscles never regain their proper tone. Repeated bladder infections can have similar effects. Gradually one's sensitivity and awareness in this area becomes dulled, and the muscles are slower to respond to nervous control.

Yoga therapy

Short of surgery, there is no medical treatment of this problem, which can be easily remedied by the appropriate yoga practices. Most important are moola bandha, vajroli mudra, naukasana and uddiyana bandha. Moola bandha and vajroli mudra should be practised in both the simple form (rapid contractions) and with the breath. Practising twice a day will bring noticeable results within a few weeks. (*See end of chapter for practice program*)

Cystitis

Strictly speaking cystitis is inflammation of the bladder and urethritis is inflammation of the urinary passage (urethra). The term cystitis is now generally used for a certain constellation of symptoms that arise from inflammation and infection of the bladder.

Signs and symptoms

The chief characteristic is a feeling that you must urinate every few minutes, and yet there is no flow or only a few drops. When urine does pass there is a terrible burning sensation. You might also feel a dull pain in the lower abdomen just above the pubic bone, or a bruised feeling around the urinary opening. Sometimes the urine has a foul smell, and may contain blood or pus.

Cause

These symptoms occur when there is inflammation of the bladder, which is usually a reaction to infection. Generally it occurs when bacteria normally present in the intestines are

188

washed over into the urinary passage, and from there ascend into the bladder. Vaginal infections can similarly be transferred to the urinary system. Although less common, it is possible for infections to pass down into the bladder from the kidneys, as in the case of tuberculosis.

Predisposing factors

Fibroids and prolapsed uterus may press on the urinary tract from outside, causing obstruction and pooling of the urine, which sometimes occurs during pregnancy also. Irritation or damage to the urethra from nearby surgery or childbirth may also make you more susceptible to infection. Tissue irritation may arise from too frequent or careless intercourse, vaginal deodorants and certain contraceptive creams. For some women, use of oral contraceptive pills predisposes them to infection, as does diabetes. Certain kinds of food may also cause an allergic reaction in the urinary system.

Medical treatment

If you develop cystitis it is important to see a doctor, for chronic infections can lead to decay of the kidneys and other serious complications. Treatment usually consists of sulpha drugs and antibiotics although surgery might also be indicated (e.g. to repair prolapse). Symptoms usually disappear within a day or two, but the full treatment may take two weeks or more. It is very important to complete the full course of treatment.

Unfortunately, the drugs which clear up urinary infections have unavoidable side effects on other systems of the body. There is almost always some kind of intestinal upset, and sometimes also nausea. Vaginitis and thrush infections of the vagina are also common. This sometimes leads to a cycle of re-infection, with the vaginal infection being swept back into the bladder. Even if the bladder infection is cleared up, there is no treatment to prevent another outbreak.

Women more susceptible

Cystitis is very common among women and it is estimated that 50% of women will have an attack at least once in their lives. Women are more susceptible than men, as the female urethra is very short and allows bacteria to reach the higher parts of the tract more easily. In women the closeness of the anus, vagina and urinary passage makes it easier for bacteria to pass between them. The bacteria that are necessary and positive in the intestines are the very same ones that cause so much havoc in the urinary system. These bacteria are often found on the skin between the anus and the genitals, and carelessness in hygiene, personally or on the part of one's mate, can be instrumental in transporting them to the vulva and urinary tract. It is therefore advisable for both partners to clear the urinary tract by passing urine after intercourse.

Cystitis is often hard to eradicate because of the possibility of cross-infection from other systems and the danger of re-infection after medical treatment. Changes in the urethra after menopause may continue this cycle. Chronic cystitis may lead to later infection of the kidneys as bacteria travel upwards from the bladder. In this case there will not only be frequent urination but acute pain in the back, and fever.

Even worse, for most women, is the devastating emotional effect of chronic cystitis. An acute attack of cystitis usually brings on an extreme physical and emotional restlessness. When attacks are frequent, this can build up into panic, or precipitate serious depression. Because it can interfere with conjugal relations, recurrent cystitis may lead to disturbed marital relationships. Due to this home life and career are often disrupted.

Major factor

Generally speaking urine is not only a sterile solution (providing no nourishment for infection) but it is also an active antiseptic (actually killing infection). Most bacteria entering the urinary system from outside are therefore killed in the urine. However, when vitality is low many of the body's delicate balances are disturbed and this is reflected in the constitution of the urine. It is for this reason that urine analysis is so helpful in diagnosis, and for this same reason that we risk urinary infections when our resistance is low.

General debility – that feeling of being always tired and run down – is the underlying cause of urinary infections. If the frustrating cycle of infection and re-infection is to be broken, then physical and emotional vitality must be restored.

Yoga therapy

Yoga practices are ideal for setting right the disturbed hormones of the body and maintaining abundant physical energies and high optimism. The prevention of urinary infections through yoga is based on a careful diet and a balanced program of asana, pranayama and meditation.

Diet and prevention

If you suffer from cystitis eat a balanced diet with plenty of whole grains and vegetables. A vegetarian diet is preferable, for it helps to avoid the excess acidity of a meat-based diet, purifies the body, conserves energy.

- Drink plenty of water, so that you urinate copiously several times a day. (Women who have scanty urine are more susceptible to infection).
- Avoid tea, coffee, alcohol, too many chillies and very spicy food. These tend to irritate the bladder and in some people cause an allergic reaction of the urinary tract.
- If urine seems to be scanty despite adequate fluid intake, drink a glass of lemon barley water twice a day, or tender coconut water.
- Make sure you have plenty of vitamin C in your diet – it helps to fight infection. This vitamin is found in all green vegetables and tomatoes, especially before cooking (vitamin C is destroyed by prolonged boiling). Fruits high in vitamin C are lemons (nimbu), oranges (mousumbi), gooseberries (amla), grapefruit, pineapple, guava and all kinds of berries.

Daily sadhana

Daily sadhana is a definite time to yourself every day, as self-culture will do much to replenish energy and build stamina. You do not need to do many practices, but you do need to practise regularly.

Shankhaprakshalana in its short form should be practised once a week for two or three months. This practice should relieve any strain on the kidneys and help to flush the whole urinary system.

Asanas: Backward bending asanas stimulate the kidneys and alternation with forward bending asanas will also massage the bladder and drain accumulations of stagnant urine. In this respect, surya namaskara is ideal for it combines important asanas of both kinds, and restores balance to a strained nervous system. Other useful asanas are supta vajrasana, ushtrasana, marjariasana, bhujangasana, dhanurasana. Matsyasana, ushtrasana and dhanurasana also exert some influence on the thymus gland in the centre of the chest. This gland has a role to play in the body's defences against infection.

Most women find that practising asanas stimulates urination, and that they must empty the bladder after asana practice even if they have urinated before commencing. This effect is enhanced when practising inverted postures, such as sarvangasana.

Pranayama: This is not just a method of breath control, it is primarily a means of revitalization through tapping sources of more subtle energy. Sheetkari and nadi shodhana are important here.

Meditation: When you are run down, both body and mind require real rest – not just diversion with books, films or outings, but genuine quiet and peace. The regular practice of meditation releases all kinds of blockages in the system and puts us in touch with the natural healing energies of the body. It takes us to that quiet place where we can be genuinely at ease with ourselves.

Practice program

Incontinence:

    Asana: Naukasana (5 rounds, hold as long as possible)
    Mudra/Bandha: Uddiyana bandha (7 rounds, standing or sitting), moola bandha rapid contraction (100 times/rest/100 times), then practise with breath (10 times), vajroli mudra rapid contraction (100 times/rest/100 times), then practise with breath (10 times).

Repeat entire program in the evening.

Cystitis:

    Asana: Surya namaskara (6 rounds), shavasana, ushtrasana or bhujangasana (15 breaths), marjariasana (15), matsyasana (30 breaths), paschimottanasana (30 breaths), sarvangasana (3–5 minutes, followed by shavasana).
    Pranayama: Sheetkari pranayama (9 rounds), nadi shodhana pranayama (10 rounds).
    Shaktkarma: Laghoo shankhaprakshalana (once a week).
    Other: Ajapa japa meditation.

Varicose Veins

If your greatest pleasure is just to 'put your feet up' to relieve tired, aching legs, then you might be developing varicose veins. The first sign of varicose veins is tired aching legs – not only after a long walk or heavy work, but routinely day after day. Very often the feet swell and become a little red, and the blue blood vessels stand out like cords above the skin, or clearly visible just below the surface. As the veins degenerate they become broad and lumpy, and may cause considerable pain around feet and ankles, behind the knees and in the groin.

Causes
Varicose veins can arise for several reasons:
- Valves in the veins of the legs become weak, so that blood flows back down the vein rather than continuing upward towards the heart. Over time, the areas around the valves become engorged, showing as ugly, protruding and painful lumps in the vein.
  Swelling of the abdomen may give rise to excessive pressure on the veins, creating an almost impassable obstruction that distends the lower veins and weakens the valves. This is common in obesity, chronic constipation and pregnancy.
  There can be one or more blood clots (thrombus) in the deep veins of the legs, forcing all the blood into the veins

194

nearer the skin, causing dilation of the blood vessel and breakdown of the valves. This is a less common cause, marked by intense pain on stretching the calf muscles.

In all cases sufferers report tiredness of the legs at the end of the day, perhaps with sharp, well-localized pains at the points of weakness. There may be swelling of the ankles, and generalized itching of the skin. The exposure of the veins also makes them vulnerable to bleeding and ulceration.

Predisposing factors

Varicose veins are more common in people of middle age or beyond, and during pregnancy (where the problem is usually only temporary). The tendency may be inherited. Varicose veins are also more likely to occur in both men and women whose occupations keep them standing for unusual lengths of time – machine operators, sales personnel, process workers, barbers, traffic police, cashiers and tellers.

Medical treatment

In very severe cases, varicose veins are treated medically through injections and surgical removal. The affected veins can be injected with a chemical that causes the walls of the blood vessel to grow together, closing off the flow of blood completely. Ligation or stripping of the veins involves tying the blood vessels closer to the skin and removing them. The blood is then carried entirely by the deeper internal system of blood vessels. Although these methods alleviate pain and remove unsightliness, they cannot remove the basic tendency towards varicose veins. It is therefore imperative that a preventative program is adopted to improve circulation so that unaffected veins do not become varicose at a later time.

General recommendations

If possible, avoid unnecessary standing, and standing still for a long time. If you must stand still, consciously contract and relax the leg muscles frequently. Otherwise walk around or walk on the spot

- Support stockings (elasticized hosiery) or crepe bandages are often helpful during the day. They are removed at night.
- Massage is effective in relieving pain and restoring circulation. It may even help overcome the problem entirely if carried out systematically and regularly.
- Rest with the feet above the head. This may be done lying on the back with the feet against the wall.

Yoga therapy

In the first place, avoid sitting on chairs, with the feet down. Rather than using a footrest, sit with the legs loosely folded (sukhasana or swastikasana) even if you are sitting in a chair or on a couch.

During pregnancy, rest in matsyakridasana. In this posture you lie on one side with the lower leg straight and the lower arm bent to cushion the head. The upper leg bends at the knee, coming over the body to rest on a pillow in front of the abdomen. This will shift the weight of the baby away from the major abdominal veins, removing the obstruction to free the flow of blood in the legs.

In cases where varicose veins are associated with chronic abdominal distension due to poor digestion, constipation, or obesity, laghoo shankhaprakshalana and kunjal kriya should be practised together with the recommended asanas. The pumping of blood from the feet and legs back to the heart is achieved by the muscles of the calves and thighs. When these muscles contract while walking, running or exercising, the pressure of the muscles 'milks' the blood upwards towards the heart.

Varicose veins can therefore be alleviated by regular activity and a systematic practise of asanas. Asanas have an added advantage in that they not only contract muscles to pump the blood, but when the posture is maintained they stretch the muscle for quite some time. This stretching renders the muscles more supple and squeezes out accumulations of stale blood.

Pawanmuktasana: Both the first and second series of pawanmuktasana are useful in managing varicose veins, especially in older people or during pregnancy. The systematic stretching of the ankles and calf muscles will squeeze out stagnant blood and stimulate the body's 'muscle pump' to push the blood towards the heart. These practices have the advantage of being performed from a sitting position, so they do not require much stamina or flexibility. The practices from the first (antirheumatic) series that should be emphasized are toe bending, ankle stretching, ankle rotation and knee bending. From the second series, leg lifting and cycling are most beneficial.

Stretching asanas: All asanas that stretch the muscles of the legs and tone the thigh and calf muscles are useful. This will include tadasana, pada hastasana, janusirshasana, paschimottanasana, sumeru (parvat) asana, and surya namaskara.

Inverted asanas: The most important practices for varicose veins are the inverted asanas – sirshasana (head-stand), sarvangasana (shoulder stand), vipareeta karani asana, and halasana (plough).

These asanas reverse the pull of gravity on the legs and allow pooled blood to drain towards the heart. This permits the damaged veins to resume their normal size and gives some relief to strained valves. Of these asanas, sirshasana is the most powerful but the most difficult. However, sarvang-asana and vipareeta karani asana are within the reach of most people. These asanas should be maintained for five to ten minutes, and they may be followed by halasana for an equal length of time. Final rest is taken in shavasana.

Avoid sitting in padmasana for long, because it cuts the blood flow at the groin. For meditation, use siddhasana or siddha yoni asana instead, or sukhasana, swastikasana. Avoid vajrasana altogether.

For maximum benefit, the recommended asanas should be practised twice a day. If you can practise only once, do so in the early evening.

197

Practice program

Varicose Veins:

Morning: Tadasana (10), pada hastasana (15 breaths), surya namaskara (3–6 rounds), shavasana, sirshasana or sarvangasana (5 minutes), halasana (5 minutes), shavasana.

Evening: Pawanmuktasana series part I (10 times each), leg lifting (5), cycling (20), shavasana, janusirshasana or paschimottanasana (15 breaths), shavasana, sirshasana or sarvangasana 5–10 minutes), halasana (5–10 minutes) shavasana.

For older people or during pregnancy:

Morning: Pawanmuktasana series part I (20 times each), leg lifting (5), cycling (10), rest with legs against wall 15 minutes).

Evening: Repeat morning program.

Yoga Sadhana
for Women

A Guide for Sadhana

At best, books on yoga are a reference and an inspiration. It remains that for maximum clarity and personal benefit, all yogic practices must be learned from a competent teacher. Once you have been instructed in the correct procedure for each asana, pranayama or meditation kriya, there is no need of written instructions or notes.

However, we are suggesting here some graded sadhana routines. These are not the only possibilities, but these sequences have shown themselves to be especially suitable for women. There is a program for absolute beginners, and further programs that may be adopted as the body becomes more flexible. Each program is designed to have maximum effect on the nervous system and hormones, and to have a systematic influence on each of the chakras. In this sense, each program is a complete sadhana and may be continued indefinitely. However, as you master the initial routines, you may wish to challenge yourself with more complex and more intense practices. The 'classical sadhana' comprises those asanas and pranayamas traditionally regarded as the most important and most powerful for spiritual awakening.

We are providing diagrams for the practices recommended here to help you connect the name of the practice with the practice itself, and as a guide to the correct sequence for your sadhana at home. Also included are the concentration points of each practice to enhance your awareness during

201

sadhana, and a list of the benefits specific to each technique. Ultimately you will be able to confirm these through your own experience and involvement with the practices as a means of self-discovery.

Practice guidance

For further information about the practices described in this section, please refer to the book *Asana Pranayama Mudra Bandha* by Swami Satyananda Saraswati, published by Yoga Publications Trust.

If you need help with any of the conditions mentioned in this book, please see a doctor for a thorough check up. Then take personal instruction from a competent yoga teacher. Do not attempt to learn from books or from casual yoga practitioners. Use this book as a guide and a reference, but remember that no book can replace the insight of an experienced teacher.

Bihar School of Yoga has ashrams and teaching centres throughout the world. If you wish to contact a qualified teacher near your home, please contact:

Bihar School of Yoga, Ganga Darshan,
Munger, 811201, Bihar, India

Tel: + 91 + 6344 222430
Fax:+ 91 + 6344 220169

Website: www.yogavision.net

For Beginners

Jala neti	daily
Shavasana	for relaxation
Titali asana	100 times
Skandha chakra	10/10
Greeva sanchalana	10 times each
Supta pawanmuktasana	3/3/3
Jhulana lurhakanasana	30 times
Chakki chalanasana	10/10
Vajrasana	15–21 breaths
Supta vajrasana	15 breaths
Ushtrasana	7–15 breaths
Marjari-asana	15 times
Shashankasana	15–30 breaths
Pranamasana	15–30 breaths
Bhramari pranayama	11 rds
Nadi shodhana pranayama	10 rds/rest/10 rds
Moola bandha	10 rds/rest/10 rds
Yoga nidra*	

---

*For this practice refer to the book *Yoga Nidra* by Swami Satyananda Saraswati, published by Yoga Publications Trust.

Jala Neti (nasal cleansing with water)

Clears mucus blockage from nasal passages. Helps alleviate cold and infection of ear, nose and throat. Relieves eye strain, improves eyesight. Helps relieve sinus congestion and sinus headache. Useful in reducing migraine headache. Tones the whole autonomic (unconscious) nervous system, particularly the nerves related to eyes, respiratory and reproductive systems. Helpful in cases of epilepsy and depression. Stimulates ajna chakra, the third eye of yogis.

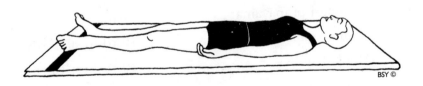

Shavasana (corpse pose)

Induces relaxation of the whole body and nervous system. To be used before and during asanas, for yoga nidra, and any time when you want quick relief from tiredness. Concentrate on each part of the body, then the whole body at once.

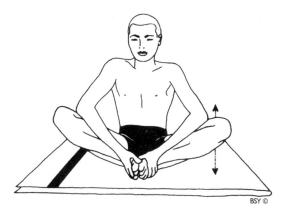

Poorna Titali Asana (full butterfly)

Loosens joints of hips, knees and ankles. Stretches inner thigh muscles and tones muscles of pelvic floor (especially important for women). Useful in relieving rheumatism and arthritis in legs and hips, and to prepare for classical meditation postures. Concentration: on sensations in joints of hip, knee and ankle.

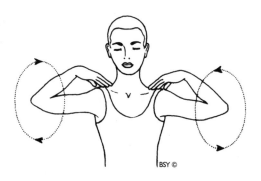

Skandha Chakra (shoulder socket rotation)

The shoulder asanas relieve the strain of driving and office work, and are helpful in cervical spondylitis and frozen shoulder. They also maintain the shape of the shoulders and chest. Concentration is on the breath, mental counting and the stretching sensation around the shoulder joint.

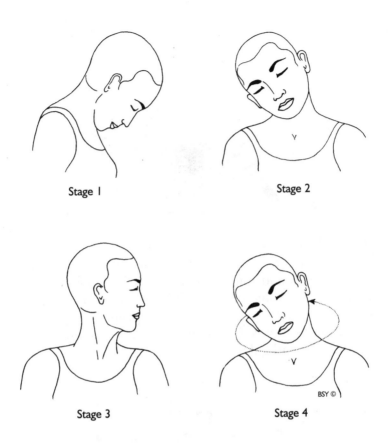

Stage 1

Stage 2

Stage 3

Stage 4

BSY ©

Greeva Sanchalana (neck movements)

These movements relax the nerves emerging from the nerve junction at the base of the neck (cervical plexus). They have a positive influence on those nerves connected with eyes and head, and respiratory system. Very helpful in relieving all kinds of headache and spondylitis. Stimulate the proper functioning of the thyroid gland. Influence the awakening of vishuddhi chakra. Concentration is on the stretching of the individual muscle groups activated by each asana.

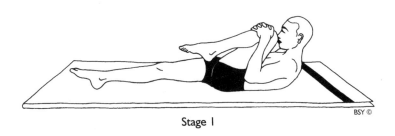

Stage 1

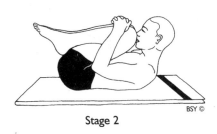

Stage 2

Supta Pawanmuktasana (leg lock posture)

Alleviates all digestive problems, especially gas formation, constipation, distension of abdomen. Stretches and tones muscles of lower back and hips. Useful in reducing weight on abdomen and buttocks, relieving lower back pain. Massages all the organs of the abdomen including intestines, bladder, uterus. Concentration is on sensation in abdomen.

Jhulana Lurhakanasana (rocking and rolling)

Helpful in digestive problems, especially constipation, gas formation. Tones liver and assists in cases of diabetes. Reduces fat on waist and hips. Helps relieve lower back pain and nervous congestion of lower back. Concentration is on stretching sensation across abdomen or on twist in the spine.

207

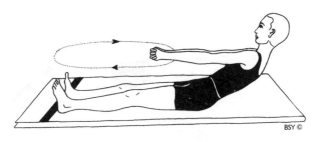

Chakki Chalanasana (churning the mill)

Tones pelvic organs and reproductive system. Relieves constipation, gas, indigestion. Reduces fat on hips and abdomen, strengthens abdominal muscles and reduces lower back pain. May be practised throughout pregnancy, and especially recommended to restore muscle tone after delivery. Excellent preparation for uddiyana bandha and nauli. Part of the shakti bandha series, which removes blockages and generates a free flow of energy. Concentration is on breath and churning of the abdomen.

Vajrasana (thunderbolt pose)

Keeps back straight and helps in relief of lower back pain. Provides alternative meditation and pranayama posture for those with sciatica. Stimulates digestion and relief of all digestive problems, especially peptic ulcer, hyperacidity, gas formation. Stimulates pingala nadi. Concentration is on flow of breath at naval or up and down the spine.

208

Supta Vajrasana (sleeping thunderbolt pose)

Influences thyroid gland, stimulates the kidneys. Helps restore hormonal balance through influence on ovaries and swadhisthana chakra. Useful in all menstrual and menopausal difficulties. Tones the nerves of spine, helps relieve lower backache. Massages abdomen and internal organs, reducing fat and eliminating digestive problems. Should be avoided in cases of prolapse. Concentration: the pressure in the lower back; swadhisthana chakra.

Ushtrasana (camel pose)

Assists in restoring hormonal balance, helpful with menstrual difficulties. An important practice for those with asthma and other respiratory complaints, stimulating the body's natural supply of cortisone. Relieves lower back ache due to tension, slipped disc or period pain. Concentration is on pressure in lower back, or centre of chest; vishuddhi chakra or anahata chakra.

209

Marjari-asana (cat stretch pose)

Stretches and bends the spine, toning spinal nerves, relieving pain anywhere in the back. Relaxes the muscles of neck and shoulders, helping to relieve headache and spondylitis. Reduces weight on abdomen and stimulates digestion, removes constipation. Tones reproductive system and restores hormonal balance. Practised during periods, will relieve stomach cramp and backache. Recommended for practise throughout pregnancy. Concentration is on contraction and relaxation of navel, or stretching of spine; manipura chakra.

210

Shashankasana (pose of the moon or hare pose)

Useful in attacks of asthma for assisting breathing. Tones
pelvic muscles, relaxes sciatic nerve to reduce pain from
sciatica. Promotes clear skin by flushing blood into face and
head. Helps to overcome tension, anxiety and anger.
Concentration is on pressure of abdomen against thighs;
manipura or swadhisthana chakra.

Pranamasana (bowing pose)

Most importantly influences all the nerves and glands in the head, having indirect influence on whole glandular system. Provides a 'freshener' when tired or drowsy. Refines the complexion of the neck and face, relaxes eyestrain. Useful for low blood pressure. Good preparation for sirshasana. Concentration is on the breath passing through pressure point where head is resting on floor; awareness of chidakasha.

Bhramari Pranayama (humming bee breath)

Facilitates exhalation, thereby relaxing heart and helping to reduce high BP. Influences the relative pressure in the breathing passages, bringing relief in asthma and emphysema. Reduces anxiety and anger. An important practice in nada yoga. Concentration is on vibration of breath at throat (vishuddhi) or forehead (ajna chakra).

212

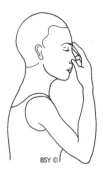

Nadi Shodhana Pranayama (psychic network purification)

Refines the breath for further stages of this most important pranayama. Induces calmness and tranquillity. Concentration is on the natural flow of the breath. Be sure to make the breath very gentle and absolutely silent. Be careful not to break the pattern of alternation.

Moola Bandha (perineum contraction)

Tones muscles of pelvic floor, preventing and relieving prolapse, restoring muscle tone after delivery, increasing control of the reproductive system. Reduces pelvic congestion, backache and menstrual difficulties. Reawakens and redirects primal energy to overcome depression. Stimulates mooladhara chakra for awakening of kundalini. Essential for practice of maithuna. Concentration on mooladhara chakra.

Intermediate Sadhana

Tadasana	5 times
Tiryaka tadasana	10 times
Kati chakrasana	20 times
Uddiyana bandha	7 times (standing)
Surya namaskara	3–12 rds
Shavasana	for relaxation
Poorwa halasana	3 times
Kandharasana	hold 7–15 breaths
Ardha shalabhasana	3 times each leg
Saral dhanurasana	hold 7–15 breaths
Janusirshasana	hold 7 breaths each
Meru wakrasana	hold 7 breaths each
Vipareeta karani asana	hold 7–15 breaths
Sirshasana stages 1 & 2	hold 15–30 breaths
Bhastrika pranayama stage 1	5 rds
Nadi shodhana (ratio 1:2)	10 rds/rest/10 rds
Antar mouna*	

---

*For this practice refer to the book *Meditations from the Tantras* by Swami Satyananda Saraswati, published by Yoga Publications Trust.

Tadasana (palm tree pose)

Stretches all the muscles of legs, abdomen and back. Opens up the chest and encourages deep breathing. Tones the abdomen and digestive system. Stimulates circulation, develops physical and mental balance. Used in the practice of shankhaprakshalana. Concentration is on breath and stretch of the whole body from top to bottom.

Tiryaka Tadasana (swaying palm tree pose)

Stretches muscles of the side, waist and hips that are rarely used in other activities. Also helps to reduce fat in these areas. Relieves stiffness and pain in back. Stretches the lungs and encourages deep breathing. Develops abdominal muscles, tones digestive system helping to eliminate gas and distension. Used in shankhaprakshalana kriya. Concentration is on stretching sensations.

215

Kati Chakrasana (waist rotating pose)

Relieves stiffness in spine and backache, tones spinal nerves. Helps redistribute waistline fat. Opens the intestines to assist proper digestion and elimination. Used in shankhaprakshalana. Concentration is on twisting of spine and relaxation.

Uddiyana Bandha (abdominal contraction)

This practice is a panacea for all digestive complaints; constipation, acidity, dyspepsia. Liver and pancreas are stimulated, making it a useful practice for diabetes. Strengthens abdominal muscles, tones all pelvic organs, stimulates and distributes prana to all parts of the body, and energy to the mind. Not to be used during pregnancy. Concentration on manipura chakra.

216

Surya Namaskara (salute to the sun)

Surya namaskara is an integral practice involving asana, pranayama and mantra, for total integration of body, mind and spirit. It has innumerable benefits, especially for women. Surya namaskara may be practised by women at any time, even during menstruation and early pregnancy. Only those women who experience heavy bleeding should refrain from this practice during their periods. This sequence stretches and strengthens all the muscles of the body and removes stiffness from every joint. It exercises the spine in various ways, toning all the spinal nerves. It encourages deep breathing, and opens blocked breathing passages. It gently stimulates the heart and improves circulation, the skin is purified and the body warmed. Excess fat is burned up. Most importantly, surya namaskara influences each and every gland in the body, bringing harmony and balance to the hormonal system. Over and above the physical, surya namaskara rapidly brings a balance between the ida and pingala nadis, thus bringing essential balance between body and mind and serving as an excellent preparation for deep relaxation and meditation.

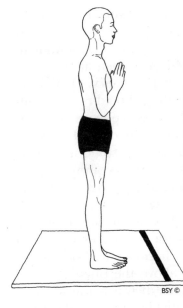

Position 1: Pranamasana (prayer pose)

Concentration on anahata chakra. Mantra: *Om Mitraya Namaha*, salutations to the friend of all. Beeja: *Om Hraam*.

Position 2: Hasta Utthanasana (raised arms pose)

Concentration on manipura chakra. Mantra: *Om Ravaye Namaha*, salutations to the shining one. Beeja: *Om Hreem*.

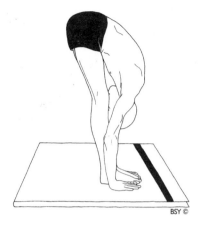

Position 3: Padahastasana (hand to foot pose)

Concentration on swadhisthana chakra. Mantra: *Om Suryaya Namaha,* salutations to he who induces activity. Beeja: *Om Hroom.*

Position 4: Ashwa Sanchalanasana (equestrian pose)

Concentration on ajna chakra. Mantra: *Om Bhanave Namaha,* salutations to he who illumines. Beeja: *Om Hraim.*

219

Position 5: Parvatasana (mountain pose)

Concentration on swadhisthana chakra. Mantra: *Om Khagaya Namaha*, salutations to he who moves quickly in the sky. Beeja: *Om Hraum.*

Position 6: Ashtanga Namaskara (salute with eight parts or points)

Concentration on manipura chakra. Mantra: *Om Pushne Namaha*, salutations to the giver of strength. Beeja: *Om Hrah.*

BSY ©

Position 7: Bhujangasana (cobra pose)
Concentration on vishuddhi chakra. Mantra: *Om Hiranya Garbhaaya Namaha*, salutations to the golden, cosmic self. Beeja: *Om Hraam*.

Position 8: Parvatasana (mountain pose)
Concentration on swadhisthana chakra. Mantra: *Om Marichaya Namaha*, salutations to the Lord of the Dawn. Beeja: *Om Hreem*.

Position 9: Ashwa Sanchalanasana (equestrian pose)
Concentration on ajna chakra. Mantra: *Om Adityaya Namaha*, salutations to the son of Aditi, the cosmic Mother. Beeja: *Om Hroom*.

Position 10: Padahastasana (hand to foot pose)
Concentration on swadhisthana chakra. Mantra: *Om Savitre Namaha*, salutations to Lord of Creation. Beeja: *Om Hraim*.

Position 11: Hasta Utthanasana (raised arms pose)
Concentration on manipura chakra. Mantra: *Om Arkaya Namaha*, salutations to he who is fit to be praised. Beeja: *Om Hraum*.

Position 12: Pranamasana (prayer pose)
Concentration on anahata chakra. Mantra: *Om Bhaskaraya Namaha*, salutations to he who leads to enlightenment. Beeja: *Om Hrah*.

Poorwa Halasana (easy plough pose)

Develops strong abdominal muscles, releases gas from digestive system. Stretches muscles of lower back and hips, and the back of the legs. Tones the pelvis and kidneys, helps reduce fat around hip girdle. Prerequisite for mastery of halasana. Concentration is on balance and breath; manipura chakra.

Kandharasana (shoulder pose)

An excellent practice for those with slipped disc, sciatica or lower back pain. Relieves pain in the upper back and shoulders. Stretches the abdomen and tones the pelvic organs and kidneys. Helpful for relief of backache and constipation during pregnancy. Prerequisite for mastery of chakrasana. Concentration is on breath in abdomen; vishuddhi chakra.

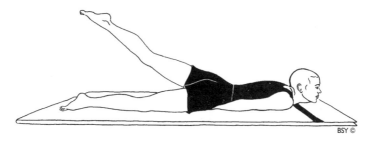

Ardha Shalabhasana (half locust pose)

Relieves sciatic and lower back pain. Develops the muscles of the legs and arms. Alleviates constipation, stimulates circulation, especially to the face, clearing the complexion. Gently stimulates the heart, and benefits low blood pressure. Concentration: on breath in abdomen; vishuddhi chakra.

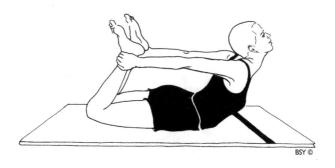

Saral Dhanurasana (easy bow pose)

Relieves pain in the upper back and shoulders. Stimulates digestion and removes fat on the abdomen. Encourages hormonal balance and menstrual regularity. Useful for asthmatics in opening blocked air passages. Preparation pose for dhanurasana. Concentration: abdomen; vishuddhi or anahata chakra.

Janu Sirshasana (head to knee pose)

Stretches the muscles of the back and behind the legs, and loosens the hip joints. Sends extra blood into the face, clearing the complexion. Tones liver, pancreas and kidneys, and regulates activity of the adrenal glands. To be avoided by those with slipped disc or sciatica. Practised in preparation for paschimottanasana. Concentration: stretching in back and legs; swadhisthana chakra.

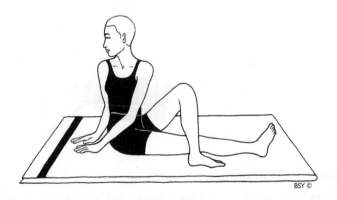

Meru Wakrasana (simple spinal twist)

Makes the spine flexible, and encourages proper alignment. Strengthens back muscles and relieves both upper and lower backache. It is therefore helpful with slipped discs, sciatica, and spondylitis. Encourages proper blood circulation and nervous tone in pelvic region, making it helpful in all kinds of women's problems. Concentration: on twisting of spine; manipura chakra.

224

Vipareeta Karani Asana (inverted pose)

Particularly important for women because it allows the uterus to find its correct position in the pelvic cavity. A must for those with prolapse, also useful for period pain and irregularity. Sends extra blood to face and head, clearing the complexion and removing fatigue. Helpful for varicose veins and also for haemorrhoids (piles). This asana stretches the neck and upper back, relieving backache and headache. Quickly brings relaxation and tranquillity. Concentration is on breath at navel; vishuddhi chakra.

Sirshasana (headstand pose) – stages 1 & 2

Brings extra blood to the face, clearing the complexion and making eyes bright. Exerts an influence on the pituitary gland – the master gland that controls the whole hormonal system. Strengthens the neck, shoulder and arm muscles in preparation for full sirshasana, and develops a sense of balance while body is inverted, must be perfected before continuing to full sirshasana.

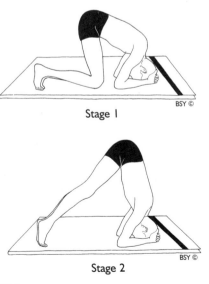

Stage 1

Stage 2

225

Bhastrika Pranayama (bellows breath)

It is a useful practice for women during labour after a few months of proper preparation. Bhastrika reduces the level of carbon dioxide in the lungs. It is an excellent practice for asthmatics and those suffering from other lung disorders. It alleviates inflammation in the throat and any accumulation of phlegm. It balances and strengthens the nervous system, inducing peace, tranquillity and one-pointedness of mind in preparation for meditation. Concentration on breath; abdominal movement; manipura chakra.

Nadi Shodhana (psychic network purification)

Ensures that the whole body is nourished by an extra supply of oxygen. Carbon dioxide is efficiently expelled and the blood is purified of toxins. The brain centres are stimulated to work nearer to their optimum capacity. It also induces tranquillity, clarity of thought and concentration, and is recommended for those engaged in mental work. It increases vitality and lowers levels of stress and anxiety by harmonising the pranas. It clears pranic blockages and balances ida and pingala nadis. causing sushumna nadi to flow, which leads to deeper states of meditation and spiritual awakening. Concentration on breath and counting; ajna chakra.

Classical Sadhana

Shavasana	for relaxation
Chakrasana	15 breaths
Bhujangasana	15 breaths
Shalabhasana	hold breath as long as possible
Dhanurasana	15 breaths
Paschimottanasana	30 breaths
Ardha matsyendrasana	15 breaths
Sarvangasana	30–50 breaths
Sirshasana	30–50 breaths
Halasana	30 breaths
Bhastrika pranayama	5 rounds
Nadi shodhana (ratio 1:1:2)	10 rds/rest/10 rds
Maha bandha	5 rds
Ajapa japa*	

---

*For this practice refer to the books *Meditations from the Tantras* by Swami Satyananda Saraswati, and *Dharana Darshan* by Swami Niranjanananda Saraswati, both published by Yoga Publications Trust.

Chakrasana (wheel pose)

Provides powerful compression of digestive and reproductive systems. Compresses both lower back and area between the shoulder blades, relieving back pain. Influences thyroid gland, ovaries, adrenal glands, kidneys for rebalance of entire hormonal system; especially important for women. Makes the body feel light and energetic. Concentration on manipura chakra.

Bhujangasana (cobra pose)

Relieves lower backache due to slipped disc or period pain. Opens congested breathing passages, and is especially helpful for asthmatics. Stimulates the kidneys, helps rectify water retention. Useful for leuccorrhoea, painful periods and absence of periods. Balances thyroid secretions, and enhances physical energy. Concentration on swadhisthana chakra.

228

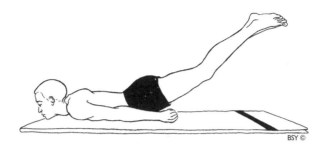

Shalabhasana (locust pose)
Strengthens the lower back and pelvic organs. Tones the
sciatic nerves relieving mild sciatica, slipped disc, and
backache. Stimulates the heart and blood circulation.
Alleviates digestive disorders. Concentration on vishuddhi
chakra.

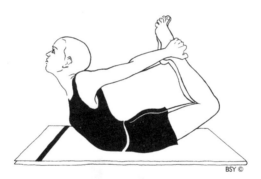

Dhanurasana (bow pose)
Relieves backache, neck and head pain. Makes the spine
supple, strengthens all the muscles of the back. Helps reduce
abdominal fat, strengthens abdominal muscles, eliminates
gas, constipation, dyspepsia (but should be avoided if you
have peptic ulcer). Tones the liver and is helpful in cases of
diabetes. Opens airways in the chest, relieves bronchitis and
asthma. Has an important influence on the hormonal system,
and minimizes menstrual and menopausal difficulties.
Influences vishuddhi, anahata and manipura chakras.
Concentration: anahata chakra.

229

Paschimottanasana (back stretching pose)

Necessary counterpose to the preceding backward bending asanas. Stretches muscles of legs and back, loosens hip joints. Helpful with diabetes and digestive disorders. Removes constipation. Stimulates kidneys and adrenal glands, replenishing vital energy. Has a strong influence on the pelvic organs and nerves, helping with all kinds of menopausal and menstrual difficulties. Quickly relaxes the mind, calming anger and bringing tranquillity. Concentration on swadhisthana chakra.

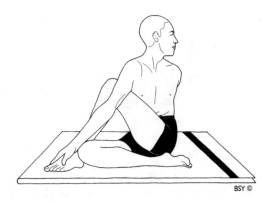

Ardha Matsyendrasana (half spinal twist)

Relaxes and strengthens muscles of back, shoulders and arms. Removes spinal stiffness, corrects alignment of spine and tones spinal nerves. Massages abdominal organs, improving digestion and relieving congestion of the reproductive system. Tones pancreas and liver, assists with diabetes. Concentration on ajna chakra.

230

Sarvangasana (shoulder stand pose)

Influences thyroid gland, balancing thyroid secretions which influence the whole metabolism. Regulates proportional body growth and weight distribution. Relieves varicose veins and haemorrhoids. Maintains an appropriate body temperature, high levels of physical vitality and an optimistic emotional outlook. Concentration on vishuddhi chakra.

Sirshasana (headstand pose) – full posture

Regarded as the most important of all asanas, influencing all aspects of physical and emotional functioning. Increases bloodflow to the brain, bringing clarity of mind and overcoming fatigue. Reduces water retention, and premenstrual pelvic congestion. Tones all the inner organs, and induces deep relaxed breathing. Most importantly, regulates the thyroid, pineal and pituitary glands which control the entire hormonal system. Of great importance to the psychological and physical health of women. Concentration on chidakasha or sahasrara chakra.

231

Halasana (plough pose)

A counterpose to sarvangasana and sirshasana. Stretches muscles in the legs, hips and back, relieves upper and lower back pain. Not for those with slipped disc or sciatica. Influences thyroid and parathyroid glands, promoting physical vitality, emotional stability. Regulates digestion, helps diabetes, haemorrhoids. Improves complexion, blood supply to head. Induces relaxation and tranquillity. Concentration on vishuddhi chakra.

Bhastrika Pranayama (bellows breath)

Full practice incorporating alternation of ida and pingala nadis. Removes tamas, harmonizes mind. Relaxes breath; starts process of pratyahara in preparation for meditation.

Nadi Shodhana Pranayama (psychic network purification)

Incorporating a ratio of 1:1:2 in further development of this pranayama, using antar kumbhaka. Essential for purification of the pranic network, for both physical health and psychological stability. Relieves anxiety, brings calmness and optimism. Helps induce pratyahara and heightens awareness of chidakasha as a preparation for meditation practices.

Maha Bandha (the great lock)

Comprises moola, uddiyana and jalandhara bandhas. Redirects psychic energy from lower chakras to higher ones. The basis for some of the most important practices of kundalini kriya yoga. Excellent preparation for meditation.

Notes

Notes